NWA

Collins

OCR GCSE Revision

Biology

Biology

OCR Gateway GCSE

Revision Guide

Contents

HT Higher Tier Content

Contents

HT Higher Tier Content

Contents

Contents

HT Higher Tier Content

Review Questions

Recap of KS3 Key Concepts

1 Name **three** structures found in both plant and animal cells. [3]

2 Why do plants cells have a cell wall? [1]

3 Why do plants cells contain chloroplasts? [1]

4 What is an enzyme? [1]

5 What is the name of the enzyme that breaks down starch? [1]

6 The enzymes we use to break down food are proteins.

How do high temperatures affect these proteins? [1]

7 What are the sections of DNA found on chromosomes, which are responsible for inherited characteristics? [1]

8 Which of the following characteristics in plants and animals are likely to be inherited?

 A flower colour in plants
 B fur colour in rabbits
 C weight in humans
 D blood group in humans
 E number of branches on a tree [3]

9 Where in the cell is DNA found? [1]

10 DNA exists as a coiled structure. What is the name we give to this structure? [1]

11 Respiration occurs in all living things. What is the purpose of respiration? [1]

12 Write down the equation for respiration. [2]

13 Plants carry out photosynthesis. Write the equation for photosynthesis. [2]

14 Plants can store the glucose produced in photosynthesis in their leaves. What is the glucose converted to for storage? [1]

15 Plants can also use the glucose produced by photosynthesis to build other molecules.

Name **two** molecules made by the plant. [2]

16 What is diffusion? [1]

17 In the lungs, where does diffusion of oxygen happen? [2]

18 How are the structures in the lungs adapted for efficient diffusion? [3]

19 Put the following in order of size, starting with the smallest:

organ   **cell**   **organ system**   **tissue** [2]

20 Construct a food chain using the organisms below:

caterpillar   **leaf**   **fox**   **bird** [2]

21 What does the arrow in a food chain show? [1]

22 Which gas is taken in by plants during respiration? [1]

23 Which gas is taken in by plants during photosynthesis? [1]

24 Which gas is the main contributor to global warming? [1]

25 What does extinct mean? [1]

26 What is a balanced diet? [3]

27 What are the **five** food groups? [5]

28 Give **three** examples of recreational drugs. [3]

29 Which organ is primarily affected by excessive alcohol consumption? [1]

30 What is the name of the substance found in red blood cells that carries oxygen? [1]

31 The diagram below shows the human respiratory system:

a) Which letter refers to the diaphragm? [1]

b) Which letter refers to the trachea? [1]

c) Which letter refers to the ribs? [1]

d) Oxygen and carbon dioxide are exchanged at structure **D**.

What is the name of this structure? [1]

e) By what process are oxygen and carbon dioxide exchanged? [1]

f) The respiratory system contains cells which produce mucus. What is the function of the mucus? [1]

Rib muscles — A
Bronchus
Bronchiole — B
D
C

Total Marks _____ / 56

Cell Structures

You must be able to:

- Describe how light microscopes and staining can be used to view cells
- Explain how the main subcellular structures are related to their functions
- Explain how electron microscopy has increased understanding of subcellular structures.

The Light Microscope

- Light microscopes are useful for viewing whole cells or large subcellular structures.
- The specimen is placed on a glass slide, covered with a cover slip and placed on the stage of the microscope.
- The eyepiece and objective lenses magnify the object.
- A lamp provides illumination.
- Magnification is calculated by multiplying the magnification of the eyepiece lens by the magnification of the objective lens.
- Typical magnification is between 40 and 2000 times larger with a resolution of about 0.2 micrometres (μm).
- Stains can be used to colour whole cells and structures within cells, e.g. the nucleus, to make them easier to see.
- Sometimes a mordant is used, which fixes the stain to the structures.

Stained Bacteria Viewed using a Light Microscope

The Electron Microscope

- Electron microscopes are useful for viewing subcellular structures, such as ribosomes, mitochondrial membranes and nuclear membranes, in detail.
- They use a beam of electrons instead of a lamp.
- The specimen is placed inside a vacuum chamber.
- Electromagnets are used instead of lenses.
- The image is viewed on a TV screen.
- Typical magnification is 1 to 2 million times larger with a resolution of 2 nanometres (nm).

Bacteria Viewed using an Electron Microscope

SI Units and Interconverting Units

1 metre (m) = 1 000 000 micrometres (μm)
$1 \mu m = 10^{-6} m$
1 metre (m) = 1 000 000 000 nanometres (nm)
$1 nm = 10^{-9} m$
To convert m to mm, multiply by 1000.
To convert mm to μm, multiply by 1000.
To convert μm to nm, multiply by 1000.

Typical Animal Cell	Bacteria	Chloroplast
10–100μm	1–10μm	0.5μm

Virus	Ribosome	Cell Membrance Thickness
80nm	25nm	20nm

Subcellular Structures

- The following structures are common to both animal and plant cells:
  - **nucleus** – controls the cell and contains genetic material in the form of chromosomes
  - **cytoplasm** – where most chemical reactions take place
  - **cell membrane** – a barrier that controls the passage of substances into and out of the cell and contains receptor molecules
  - **mitochondria** – contain the enzymes for cellular respiration and are the site of respiration.
- Additionally, plant cells contain:
  - **cell wall** – made from cellulose and provides structural support
  - **vacuole** – contains cell sap, which provides support
  - **chloroplasts** – contain chlorophyll and are the site of photosynthesis.

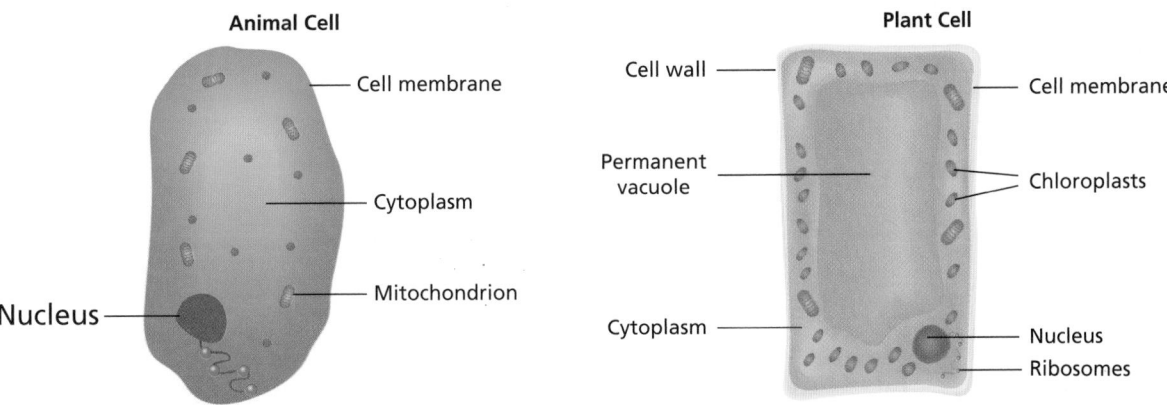

Types of Cells

- **Prokaryotes**, e.g. bacteria, have no nucleus – the nuclear material lies free within the cytoplasm.
- They may contain additional DNA in the form of a **plasmid**.
- **Eukaryotes**, e.g. human cheek cell, amoeba, plant cell, have a nucleus bound by a nuclear membrane.
- In eukaryotes, the cell wall is only present in plant cells.

A Prokaryote

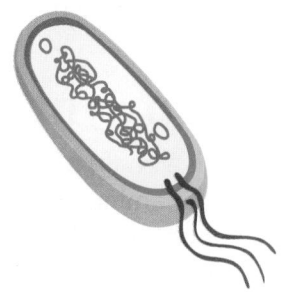

Quick Test

1. The eyepiece lens of a light microscope is ×10 and the objective lens is ×4. What is the total magnification?
2. Which part of a cell is:
   a) the site of respiration?
   b) the site of photosynthesis?
   c) a barrier controlling what passes in and out of the cell?
   d) where most chemical reactions take place?
3. Name **two** structures found in plant cells, but not in animal cells.

Key Words

magnification
resolution
stain
mordant
receptor molecules
chlorophyll
prokaryote
plasmid
eukaryote

What Happens in Cells

You must be able to:

- Describe the structure of DNA
- **HT** Describe the process of protein synthesis and explain how the structure of DNA affects the synthesis of proteins
- Explain how enzymes work.

DNA

- **DNA** (deoxyribonucleic acid) is a **polymer** made of two strands that are in the form of a **double helix**.
- Each strand is made up of **nucleotides**.
- Each nucleotide consists of a sugar, a phosphate group and a base.
- There are four possible bases:

Adenine	A	Thymine	T
Cytosine	C	Guanine	G

- When the two strands pair up:
  - **A** always joins with **T**
  - **C** always joins with **G**.

C A A C A T C G C A A C

G T T G T A G C G T T G

- A sequence of three nucleotides is called a triplet.

Double Helix

HT Protein Synthesis

- A protein is a chain of amino acids.
- The order of amino acids determines the protein that is made.
- Each triplet on the DNA codes for a particular amino acid.
- Protein synthesis involves transcription and translation.
- **Transcription:**
  - Occurs in the nucleus of the cell.
  - The section of DNA that codes for a protein 'unzips'.
  - A complementary strand of messenger RNA (mRNA) forms on one DNA strand.
  - The mRNA peels off and moves into the cytoplasm.
- **Translation:**
  - Occurs in the cytoplasm.
  - The mRNA attaches to a ribosome.
  - Transfer RNA (tRNA) brings the correct amino acid for each triplet code.

Enzymes

- Enzymes are biological catalysts and increase the rate of chemical reactions inside organisms.
- Enzymes are made of proteins and the amino acid chain is folded to make a shape into which **substrates** (substances) can fit.
- The place where the substrate fits is called the **active site**.
- Enzymes are specific and only substrate molecules with the correct shape can fit into the active site. This is called the 'lock and key' hypothesis.
- Enzymes are **denatured** when they lose their shape. The substrate no longer fits and the enzyme does not work.

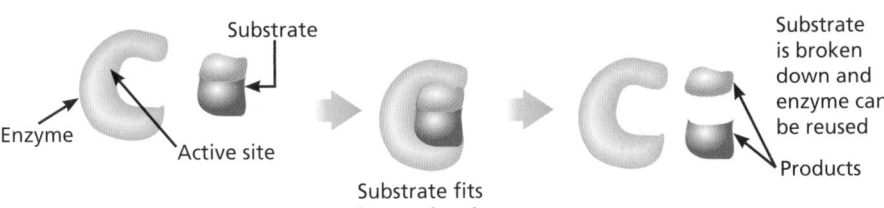

Factors Affecting Enzyme Action

- The rate of enzyme action is affected by temperature, pH, substrate concentration and enzyme concentration.
- High temperatures and deviation from the optimum (ideal) pH cause enzymes to lose their shape and become denatured.
- Low temperatures slow down the rate of reaction.
- Different enzymes have different optimum pH levels depending on where they act in the body.
- Many human enzymes have an optimum temperature of 37°C as this is normal human internal body temperature.
- As substrate concentration increases, the rate of enzyme activity increases to the point where all the enzymes present are being used.
- As enzyme concentration increases, the rate of enzyme activity increases to the point where all the substrate present is being used.

Presenting Data
How pH affects invertase activity

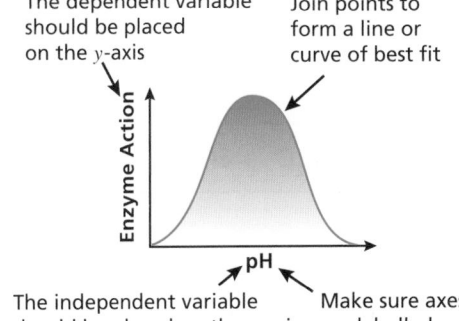

Interpreting Data
How temperature affects invertase activity

Quick Test

1. What are the **three** components that make up a nucleotide?
2. What base pairs with **a)** adenine and **b)** cytosine?
3. **HT** Where do **a)** transcription and **b)** translation take place?
4. Explain what is meant by the 'lock and key' hypothesis.

Respiration

You must be able to:

- Describe cellular respiration
- Compare aerobic and anaerobic respiration
- Describe the synthesis and breakdown of large molecules such as proteins, carbohydrates and lipids.

Cellular Respiration

- Cellular respiration happens inside the cells of all plants and animals. It occurs continuously and is controlled by enzymes.
- It is an **exothermic** reaction and releases energy in the form of a high energy molecule called ATP (adenosine triphosphate).

Aerobic Respiration

- **Aerobic respiration** (in the presence of oxygen) happens in almost all organisms all the time.

glucose + oxygen ⟶ carbon dioxide + water (+ energy released)

$$C_6H_{12}O_6 + 6O_2 \longrightarrow 6CO_2 + 6H_2O \text{ (+ energy released)}$$

Anaerobic Respiration

- Cellular respiration can also happen anaerobically (without oxygen).
- In animal cells, **anaerobic respiration** produces lactic acid:

glucose ⟶ lactic acid (+ energy released)

- Anaerobic respiration occurs when oxygen cannot be delivered to the cells fast enough, for example during vigorous activity.
- When exercise stops there is an **oxygen debt**, which must be paid back to remove the lactic acid which has accumulated in the cells.
- This is why the breathing rate is so fast.
- In yeast, anaerobic respiration produces ethanol:

> **Key Point**
>
> Anaerobic respiration in yeast is called fermentation.
>
> In everyday life, ethanol tends to be called alcohol.

glucose ⟶ carbon dioxide + ethanol (+ energy released)

	Where it Occurs	Oxygen	Breakdown of Glucose	ATP Yield per Mole of Glucose	Energy Released per Mole of Glucose
Aerobic	Mitochondria	Needed	Complete	38	2900kJ
Anaerobic	Cytoplasm	Not needed	Incomplete	2	120kJ

Breakdown of Biological Molecules

- We take in carbohydrates, proteins and lipids in our diet.
- These are all large molecules called polymers.
- During digestion, they are broken down by enzymes into smaller molecules, called monomers.
- Fats need to be broken down into small droplets to make them more digestible. This is called emulsification.
- In the small intestine, bile is responsible for emulsifying fats.

Name of Enzyme	Substrate it Acts Upon	Name of Monomers Produced
Carbohydrase	Carbohydrate	Glucose
Protease	Proteins	Amino acids
Lipase	Lipids (fats)	Fatty acids, glycerol

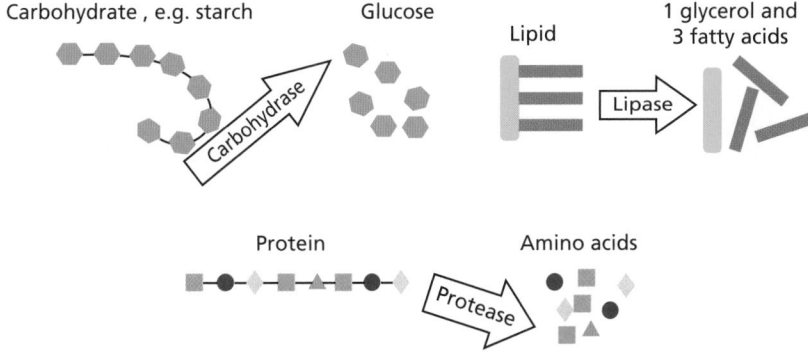

Synthesis of Biological Molecules

- Glucose, amino acids, glycerol and fatty acids are transported by the blood to the cells in the body.
- Inside the cells:
  - Glucose can be used in respiration.
  - Amino acids can be used to make useful proteins, e.g. enzymes and hormones.
  - Glycerol and fatty acids can be used to make useful lipids.
- Breakdown of proteins, carbohydrates and lipids produces the building blocks to synthesise the many different types of molecules that our bodies need to function.

Quick Test

1. What is the word equation for aerobic respiration?
2. Where does aerobic respiration happen?
3. What are the products of fermentation?
4. What are the names of the enzymes that break down:
   a) proteins?
   b) fats?
   c) carbohydrates?

Key Words

exothermic
aerobic respiration
anaerobic respiration
oxygen debt
polymer
monomer
emulsification

Photosynthesis

You must be able to:

- Name organisms that photosynthesise and state why they are important
- Describe photosynthesis
- Describe experiments to investigate photosynthesis
- **HT** Explain factors that affect the rate of photosynthesis.

Photosynthesis

- Green plants and algae make their own food using photosynthesis.
- They trap light from the Sun to fix carbon dioxide with hydrogen (from water) to form glucose.
- The glucose is used by the plants and algae to build larger molecules, such as complex carbohydrates and proteins.
- These are then passed onto animals in the food chain.

- The equation for photosynthesis is:

$$\text{carbon dioxide} + \text{water} \xrightarrow[\text{chlorophyll}]{\text{light energy}} \text{glucose} + \text{oxygen}$$

- Photosynthesis is an endothermic reaction.
- Photosynthesis occurs inside the chloroplasts, which contain chlorophyll.

Investigating Photosynthesis

- Watching gas bubble up from *Cabomba*, a type of pond weed, is a good visual demonstration of photosynthesis.
- The experiment can be used to investigate how the amount of light or the temperature of the water affects the rate of photosynthesis.

A student carried out an investigation into the effect of light on photosynthesis.
They placed the apparatus shown on page 15 at different distances from a desk lamp and counted the number of bubbles produced in 5 minutes.
The results are shown in the table.

Palisade Cell

Packed with chloroplasts for photosynthesis.

Glass tube

Water

Beaker

Funnel

Pond weed

Distance of Lamp (cm)	0	5	10	15	20	25
Number of Bubbles	108	65	6	2	0	0

Evaluate the method and suggest possible improvements for further investigations.

Evaluation:

- It would have been better to use smaller distance intervals, e.g. 2.5cm, because there were not many bubbles after 5cm.
- It would have been difficult to count the bubbles at 0 because they were quite fast. It would have been better to collect them and measure the volume of gas produced.
- Another improvement would be to count for a longer time as there were so few bubbles at 10 and 15cm.

When evaluating the method, consider:
- Was the equipment suitable?
- Were there enough results?
- Was it a fair test?
- Were the results reliable?

When suggesting improvements always state why they would make the experiment or results better.

Factors Affecting Photosynthesis

- The optimum temperature for photosynthesis is around 30°C.
- At 45°C, the enzymes involved start to become denatured.
- Increased carbon dioxide levels increase the rate of photosynthesis.

HT In the second graph on the right, the rate stops increasing because either temperature or light becomes the limiting factor.

- Increasing the light intensity, increases the rate of photosynthesis.
- Light intensity obeys an inverse square law – if you double the distance you quarter the light intensity. In the experiment above you should use the inverse number of the distance squared as a measure of light intensity.

HT In the third graph, the rate stops increasing because temperature or carbon dioxide becomes the limiting factor.

Effect of Temperature

Rate of Photosynthesis

45°C

Temperature

Effect of Carbon Dioxide Concentration

Rate of Photosynthesis

Concentration of Carbon Dioxide

Effect of Light Intensity

Rate of Photosynthesis

Light Intensity

Quick Test

1. What are a) the reactants and b) the products of photosynthesis?
2. Where in the cell does photosynthesis occur?
3. Why does photosynthesis stop at temperatures over 50°C?

Key Words

photosynthesis
endothermic
chlorophyll
HT limiting factor

Supplying the Cell

You must be able to:

- Explain how substances are transported by diffusion, osmosis and active transport
- Describe the stages of mitosis
- Give examples of specialised cells
- Explain the role of stem cells.

Transport of Substances In and Out of Cells

- Substances need to pass through cell membranes to get in and out of cells. This can happen in one of three ways:
  - **Diffusion** – the net movement of particles from an area of high concentration to an area of low concentration, i.e. along a concentration gradient.
  - **Active transport** – molecules move against the concentration gradient, from an area of low concentration to an area of high concentration. This requires energy.
  - **Osmosis** – the net movement of water from a dilute solution to a more concentrated solution through a **partially permeable** membrane.

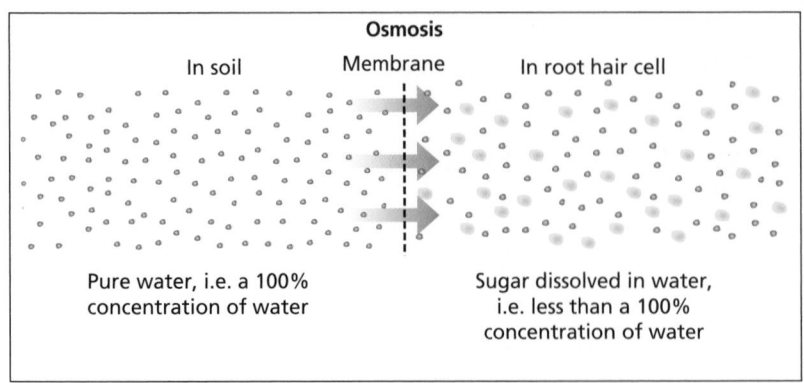

Key Point

Oxygen and glucose move into cells by diffusion. Carbon dioxide moves out of cells by diffusion.

Key Point

A concentration gradient is a measurement of how the concentration of something changes from one place to another.

Key Point

Glucose is moved from the intestine to the blood stream by active transport. Minerals from the soil move into root hair cells by active transport.

Key Point

A dilute solution has a high water potential. A concentrated solution has a low water potential. In osmosis, water diffuses from a region of high water potential to an area of low water potential.

Mitosis

- Mitosis is the division of cells to produce new cells.
- New cells are needed to replace those that die or are damaged.
- The growth and division of cells is called the **cell cycle**.
- The stages of mitosis are:
  1. Parent cell contains chromosomes.
  2. Chromosomes are copied.
  3. Chromatids (the two sets of chromosomes) pull apart.
  4. Two new cells created, each identical to parent.

Stages of Mitosis

Cell Differentiation

- Cell differentiation is when one cell changes into another type of cell.
- In animals this usually happens at an early stage of development and occurs to create specialised cells.
- In mature animal cells, differentiation is mostly restricted to replacement and repair.
- Many plant cells, however, maintain the ability to differentiate.
- Here are some examples of specialised cells:

Root Hair Cells	Ovum (Egg Cell)	Xylem	Sperm Cell	Nerve Cells
Tiny hair-like extensions increase the surface area of the cell for absorption.	Large cell that can carry food reserves for the developing embryo.	Long, thin, hollow cells used to transport water through the stem and root.	Has a tail, which allows it to move.	Long, slender axons that can carry nerve impulses.

Stem Cells

- Stem cells are undifferentiated cells that can differentiate to form specialised cells, such as muscle cells or nerve cells.
- Human stem cells can come from human **embryos**, in umbilical cord blood from new born babies or from adult **bone marrow**.
- Embryonic stem cells can differentiate into any type of cell.
- Adult stem cells can only differentiate into the cells of the type of tissue from which they came.
- Plant stem cells are found in **meristematic** tissue, which is usually in the tips of shoots and roots.
- Stem cells have the potential to provide replacement cells and tissues to treat Parkinson's disease, burns, heart disease and arthritis. The tissues made will not be rejected by the body.
- Stem cells can also be used for testing new drugs.

Key Point

There are ethical issues surrounding the use of stem cells, for example: Is destroying embryos taking a life? Is it right to dispose of human embryos? And who decides which people should benefit from such a treatment?

Key Words

diffusion
active transport
osmosis
partially permeable
cell cycle
embryos
bone marrow
meristematic

Quick Test

1. What are the differences between diffusion and active transport?
2. Name **two** molecules that diffuse into cells.
3. Why is mitosis important?
4. Where do **a)** embryonic and **b)** adult stem cells come from?

The Challenges of Size

You must be able to:

- Explain why organisms need exchange surfaces and transport systems
- Describe substances that need to be exchanged and transported
- Describe the human circulatory system.

Exchange Surfaces and Transport Systems

- Exchange surfaces allow efficient transport of materials across them by mechanisms such as diffusion and active transport.
- In simple **unicellular** organisms, the cell membrane provides an efficient exchange surface.
- **Multicellular** organisms, which have a smaller surface area to volume ratio, have developed specialised exchange surfaces.
- The following substances all need to be exchanged and transported:
    - oxygen and carbon dioxide
    - dissolved food molecules, e.g. glucose and minerals
    - **urea** (waste product from breakdown of proteins)
    - water.
- An efficient exchange system should have:
    - a large surface area to volume ratio
    - membranes that are very thin so diffusion distance is short
    - a good supply of transport medium (e.g. blood, air, etc.).

Two groups of students investigated how quickly coloured water diffused into agar cubes with a surface area of 24cm².

They repeated each test three times. Here are the results of one of their tests:

	Time Taken to Diffuse in Seconds			Average (Mean)
	1	2	3	
Group 1	122	124	126	124
Group 2	136	128	150	138

The data from Group 1 is **repeatable**. This is because all three times recorded are near to each other.

The data is not **reproducible**. This is because the data from Group 1 is different to Group 2.

The data from Group 1 is more **precise** as all the times are near the mean.

Key Point

The alveoli are the site of gas exchange in the lungs.

A Single Alveolus and a Capillary

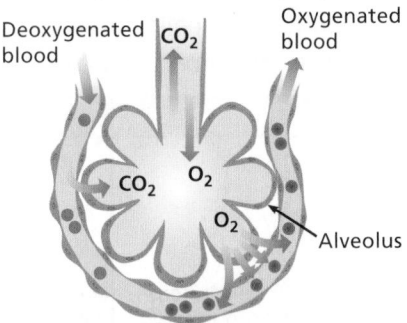

Deoxygenated blood — CO_2 — Oxygenated blood — CO_2 — O_2 — O_2 — Alveolus

Key Point

The villi in the small intestine provide an exchange surface for the absorption of dissolved food molecules, such as glucose, amino acids, fatty acids and minerals.

A single villus

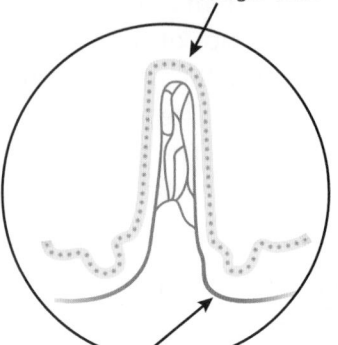

Capillary

You need to remember to evaluate data in terms of accuracy, precision, repeatability and reproducibility.

Measuring in second intervals is more accurate than measuring in minutes.

The Human Circulatory System

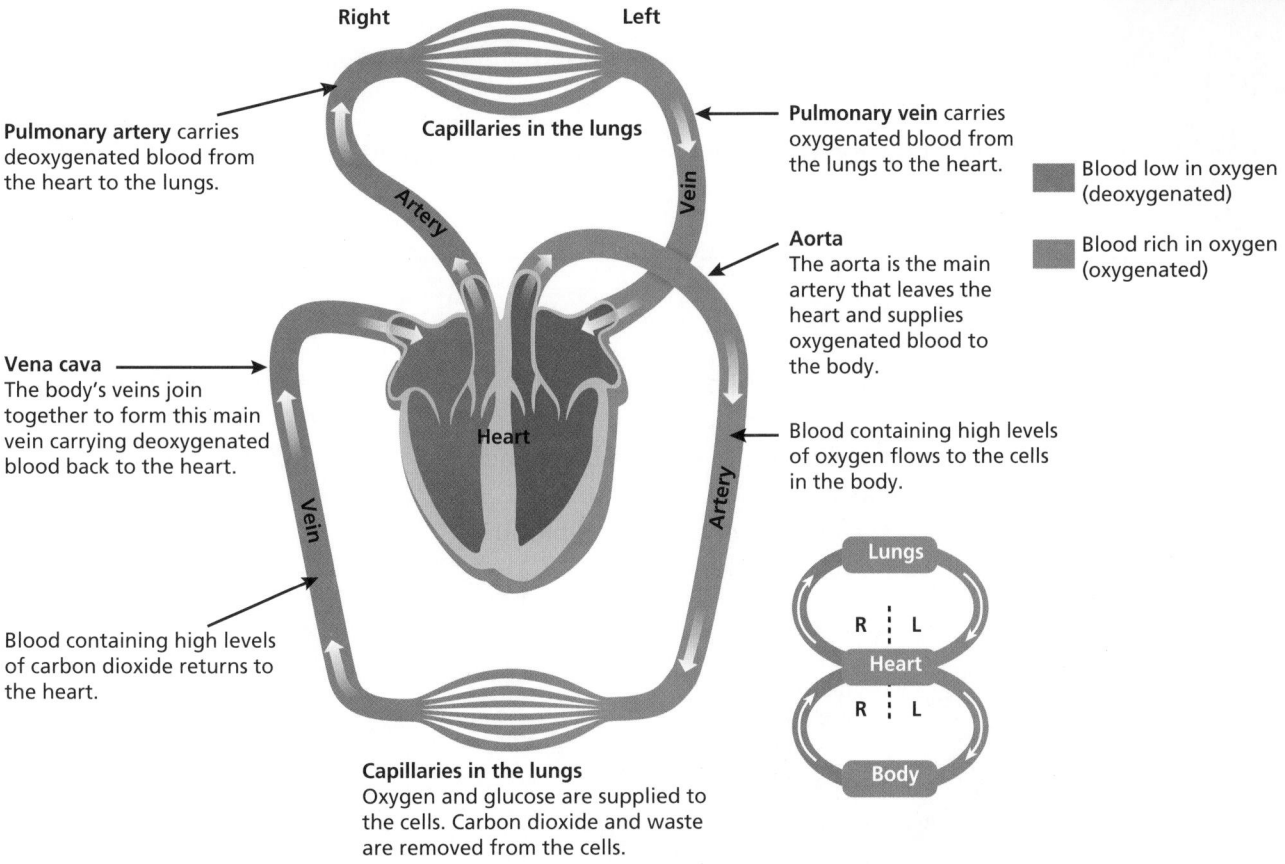

Right **Left**

Capillaries in the lungs

Pulmonary artery carries deoxygenated blood from the heart to the lungs.

Pulmonary vein carries oxygenated blood from the lungs to the heart.

Blood low in oxygen (deoxygenated)

Blood rich in oxygen (oxygenated)

Aorta
The aorta is the main artery that leaves the heart and supplies oxygenated blood to the body.

Vena cava
The body's veins join together to form this main vein carrying deoxygenated blood back to the heart.

Heart

Blood containing high levels of oxygen flows to the cells in the body.

Blood containing high levels of carbon dioxide returns to the heart.

Lungs

R | L

Heart

R | L

Body

Capillaries in the lungs
Oxygen and glucose are supplied to the cells. Carbon dioxide and waste are removed from the cells.

- Humans have a double circulatory system with two loops:
  - one from the heart to the lungs
  - one from the heart to the body.
- The advantage of a double circulatory system is that it can achieve a higher blood pressure and, therefore, a greater flow of blood (and oxygen) to tissues.
- Substances transported by the circulatory system include oxygen, carbon dioxide, dissolved food molecules, hormones, antibodies, urea and other waste products.
- The right side of the circulatory system carries deoxygenated blood. The left side carries oxygenated blood.

Key Words

unicellular
multicellular
urea
repeatable
reproducible
precise
deoxygenated
oxygenated

Quick Test

1. What are **three** features of an efficient exchange system?
2. Why do multicellular organisms need specialised exchange systems?
3. What are the advantages of a double circulatory system?

The Heart and Blood Cells

You must be able to:

- Explain how the structures of the heart and blood vessels are adapted to their functions
- Explain how red blood cells and plasma are adapted to their functions.

The Heart

- The heart pumps blood to the lungs and around the body.
- It is made mostly of muscle.
- The left ventricle needs to pump blood round the whole body and, therefore, has thicker, more muscular walls.
- The valves between atria and ventricles and ventricles and blood vessels are to prevent blood flowing backwards.

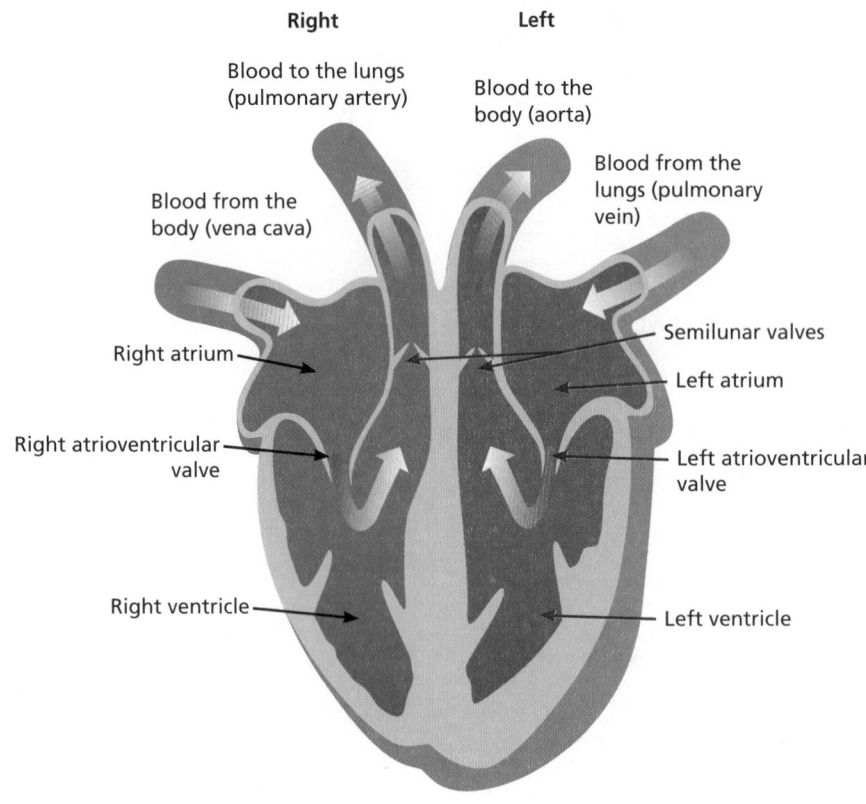

Right

Blood to the lungs (pulmonary artery)

Blood from the body (vena cava)

Right atrium

Right atrioventricular valve

Right ventricle

Left

Blood to the body (aorta)

Blood from the lungs (pulmonary vein)

Semilunar valves

Left atrium

Left atrioventricular valve

Left ventricle

Flow of Blood Through the Heart

From body to right atrium

↓

To right ventricle

↓

To lungs via pulmonary artery

↓

From lungs to left atrium via pulmonary vein

↓

To left ventricle

↓

To body via aorta

Red Blood Cells

- Red blood cells carry oxygen.
- They have a biconcave disc shape that maximises the surface area for absorbing oxygen.
- They contain haemoglobin, which binds to oxygen in the lungs and releases it at the tissues.
- Red blood cells do not have a nucleus, which means there is more space to carry oxygen.

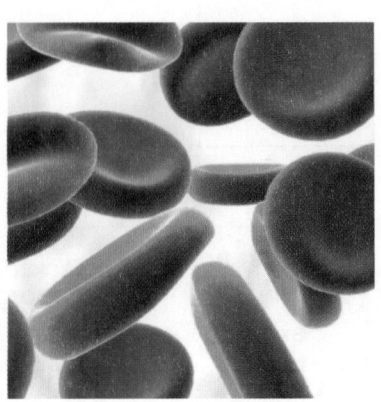

Blood Vessels

- There are three types of blood vessel: arteries, veins and capillaries.

Artery **Vein** Valve **Capillary**

Lumen Lumen

Note: capillaries are much smaller than veins or arteries

- Arteries carry blood away from the heart.
- Veins carry blood to the heart.
- Capillaries deliver nutrients to cells and remove waste products from them.
- Arteries have thick outer walls with thick layers of elastic and muscle fibres because they have to carry blood under high pressure.
- Veins have a large lumen (cavity or opening) and thin walls, since blood is under low pressure.
- Veins also have valves to stop blood flowing backwards.
- Capillaries have very thin, permeable walls to allow substances to easily pass into and out of tissues.

A Capillary Network in a Muscle

Artery rich in oxygen and glucose

Tissue cells

Vein rich in carbon dioxide and waste

Close-Up of a Capillary Vessel

Cell

Capillary wall (one cell thick)

Carbon dioxide and waste   Oxygen and glucose   Blood flow

Plasma

- Plasma is the pale coloured liquid part of blood. It transports:
  - hormones
  - antibodies
  - nutrients, such as glucose, amino acids, minerals and vitamins
  - waste substances, such as carbon dioxide and urea.

Plants, Water and Minerals

You must be able to:

- Explain how plants take in water and minerals
- Describe the processes of translocation and transpiration
- Explain how xylem and phloem are adapted to their functions
- Explain how water uptake in plants is measured and factors that affect it.

Mineral and Water Uptake in Plants

- Plants need to take in water for photosynthesis and minerals for general health. These are taken in through the roots.
- Root hair cells have a large surface area to maximise absorption of water and minerals.
- Their cell membrane is thin, which also helps absorption.
- Water enters root hair cells by osmosis.
- Minerals enter root hair cells by active transport.
- There are three essential minerals that plants need to be healthy:
  - nitrates
  - phosphates
  - potassium.

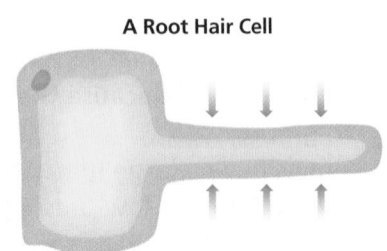

A Root Hair Cell

Transport Systems in Plants

- Plants have two types of transport tissue: xylem and phloem.
- The xylem and phloem are found in the stem of the plant.
- Movement of glucose from the leaf to other parts of the plant by phloem tissue is called **translocation**.

Cross-Section of a Stem

Phloem vessels carry food substances up and down the plant

Xylem

Phloem

Xylem vessels carry water up from the roots

Tissue Properties	Xylem Vessels	Phloem Vessels
What does it transport?	Xylem transports water and minerals from the soil to other parts of the plant.	Phloem transports the glucose made in the leaf by photosynthesis to other parts of the plant.
How is it adapted to its function?	Xylem vessels are made of dead cells. They have a thick cell wall and hollow lumen. There are no cell contents and no end cell walls, therefore, there is a continuous column for water to move up.	Phloem vessels are made of living cells. They have lots of mitochondria to release energy to move substances by active transport.

Transpiration

- Transpiration is the upward flow of water from roots to leaves, from where it evaporates into the atmosphere.

- The more water a plant loses via the leaves, the more water it will need to take in through the roots.

$$\text{rate of transpiration} = \frac{\text{volume water lost}}{\text{time}}$$

- A **potometer** can be used to measure water uptake.
- As water is lost from the leaves, the air bubble moves to the left.
- Water is lost through **stomata** in the leaves.
- Plants can close stomata to reduce water loss. However, this closure also reduces the intake of carbon dioxide, which will limit photosynthesis.

A Potometer

Water Uptake and Transpiration

- The factors that affect water uptake and transpiration are:
  - wind velocity
  - temperature
  - humidity.

How Wind Velocity Affects Transpiration	How Temperature Affects Transpiration	How Humidity Affects Transpiration
Positive correlation (non-linear)	Positive correlation (linear)	Negative correlation (linear)

You need to analyse distributions of data and predict the shape of graphs.

Extrapolation: by extending the line (dotted line) it is possible to predict that the rate of transpiration at 35°C will be 16.5ml/hour.

Negative correlation: as one variable increases, the other decreases.

Positive correlation: as one variable increases, so does the other.

Linear: the graph is a straight line.

Scaling Up: Revise

Practice Questions

Cell Structures

1 Complete the table below using a tick or cross to indicate if the structures are present or absent in each of the cells.

Structure / Cell	Cell Wall	Cytoplasm	Nuclear Membrane	Cell Membrane	Chloroplasts
Plant					
Animal					
Bacterium					

[3]

2 Haematoxylin and eosin is a common stain made of two components.
The table below gives some information about each of the components.

Component	Haematoxylin	Eosin
Colour	black / blue	pink
Type of stain	basic	acidic
Structures stained	nucleic acids, ribosomes	mitochondria, cytoplasm, collagen

The diagram below shows a cheek cell that has been stained with haematoxylin and eosin.

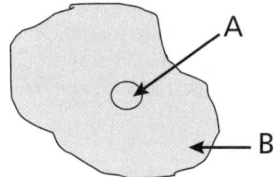

a) Use the information from the table to decide which colour each of the following areas would appear when the cell is viewed using a light microscope:

   i) Area A [1]

   ii) Area B [1]

b) The light microscope used to view the cell had an eyepiece lens with a magnification of 10 and an objective lens with a magnification of 40.

   What is the total magnification? [1]

3 The table below gives the diameter of two different cells.

Cell	Diameter
A	3000nm
B	4.5µm

Which cell is larger? [1]

4 Use the words below to label the diagrams.

Nucleus   **Vacuole**   **Chloroplast**   **Cell membrane**
  Cytoplasm   **Cell wall**   **Animal cell**   **Plant cell**

[8]

Total Marks _____ / 15

What Happens in Cells

1 The figure on the right shows the bases on one strand of a DNA molecule.

a) Complete the base sequence on the second strand by writing the letters in the boxes.

[3]

b) Complete the sentences below using the correct words.

nucleotides   phosphate group   polymer   base

DNA is a _____. It is made from _____,

which consist of a sugar, _____ and

_____.

[4]

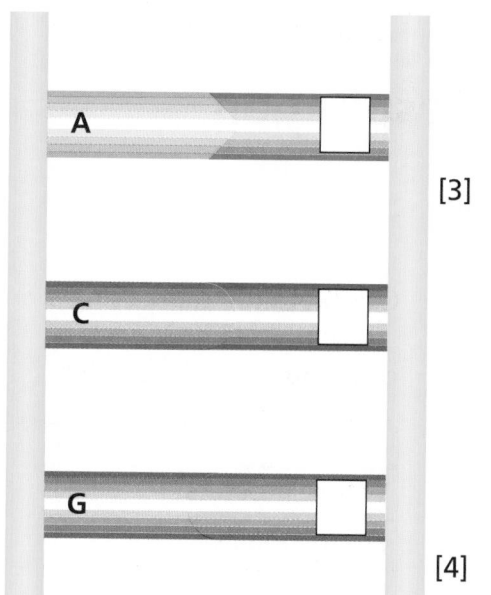

c) The two chains of the DNA molecule form a coiled structure.

What is the name of this structure?

[1]

d) HT A sequence of three bases is called a triplet code.

What is the function of the triplet code?

[1]

Practice Questions

2 The diagram below is about enzyme action.

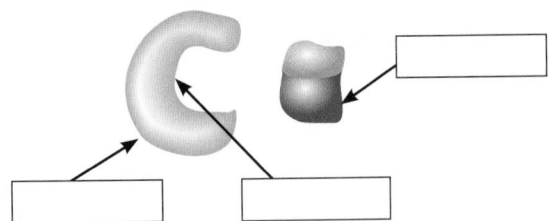

a) Label the enzyme, substrate and active site. [3]

b) Describe what will happen to the enzyme at temperatures above 50°C. [2]

c) Name a factor, other than temperature, that affects enzyme activity. [1]

d) Complete the sentences below by choosing the correct word.

Enzymes are **carbohydrates / proteins / fats**.

They are biological **substrates / monomers / catalysts**. [2]

Total Marks .... / 17

Respiration

1 The table below compares aerobic and anaerobic respiration.

Complete the table using words from the list.

complete   incomplete   cytoplasm   low   high   mitochondria

	Aerobic	Anaerobic
Where it occurs		
Energy release		
Breakdown of glucose		

[6]

2 Complete the equation for aerobic respiration:

.... + ... → .... + ... + energy [4]

Total Marks .... / 10

Photosynthesis

1 Complete the word equation for photosynthesis:

_____ + _____ $\xrightarrow{\text{light energy}}$ _____ + _____ [4]

2 The cell on the right is packed with subcellular structures that contain the enzymes for photosynthesis.

a) What is the name of this cell? [1]

b) What is the name of the structures that are the site of photosynthesis? [1]

c) What is the name of the green pigment inside these structures? [1]

> **Total Marks** _____ / 7

Supplying the Cell

1 The drawing below shows a single celled organism called an amoeba.

a) Name **two** substances that pass through the cell membrane into the amoeba. [2]

b) By what process will the carbon dioxide produced by respiration move out of the amoeba? [1]

c) Choose the correct word to complete the sentence below.

Amoeba is a **unicellular / multicellular** organism. [1]

2 A slice of raw potato is weighed and placed in a beaker of water for several hours.
The potato is then taken out, dried and reweighed.
At the start of the experiment, the potato slice weighed 4g.
After soaking in water, it weighed 6.3g.

a) Calculate the increase in mass. [1]

b) Explain why the potato increased in mass. [3]

3 Complete the sentences by choosing the best words from the selection below.

You do **not** have to use all the words.

low   between   chloroplasts   energy   uneven   against   net   high   slow

Diffusion is the _____ movement of particles from an area of _____

concentration to an area of _____ concentration. Active transport moves particles

_____ a concentration gradient and requires _____.   [5]

4 Which of the following statements best describes osmosis?   [1]

  A Osmosis is the movement of particles from an area of high water potential to an area of low water potential.

  B Osmosis is the movement of particles from an area of low water potential to an area of high water potential.

  C Osmosis is the movement of water from an area of high water potential to an area of low water potential.

  D Osmosis is the movement of water from an area of low water potential to an area of high water potential.

5 Mitosis is a form of cell division that produces new cells.

Give **two** reasons why the body needs to produce new cells.   [2]

6 Cells can differentiate to form specialised cells.

  a) Match the drawing of each cell to its name by a drawing a line between them.

Cell	Name
	Palisade cell
	Sperm cell
	Red blood cell
	Nerve cell

[3]

  b) Which type of cell usually differentiates at an early stage of development?   [1]

    A Animal

    B Plant

7 Human stem cells can be made to differentiate into different types of cells.

From where are adult stem cells obtained? [1]

8 Many people are against using embryonic stem cells to treat human diseases.

Give **one** ethical reason why people may be against this. [1]

> **Total Marks** .... / 22

The Challenges of Size

1 The diagram below shows an exchange system in humans.

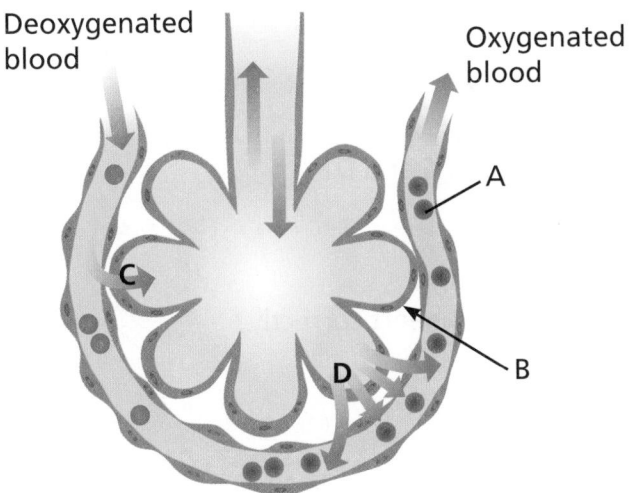

Deoxygenated blood

Oxygenated blood

A

C

D

B

a) In what organ of the body would you find this exchange system? [1]

b) What structure is letter **A**? [1]

c) What structure is letter **B**? [1]

d) Movement of what substance is represented by arrow **C**? [1]

e) Movement of what substance is represented by letter **D**? [1]

> **Total Marks** .... / 5

Practice Questions

The Heart and Blood Cells

1 The diagram below shows the human heart.

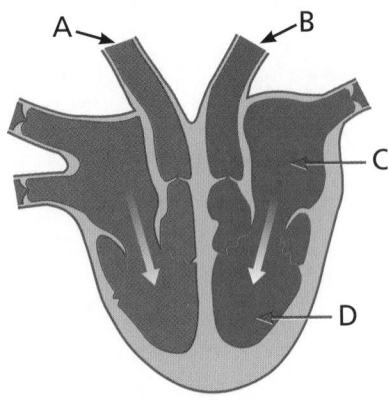

a) What are the names of the parts labelled **A–D**? [4]

b) What is the name of the valve found between parts **C** and **D**? [1]

c) What is the function of the valve found between parts **C** and **D**? [1]

d) When blood flows through part **A**, where is it going? [1]

2 Which of the following completes the sentence about the heart correctly?

The walls of the left ventricle...

A are thinner than the walls of the right ventricle.
B are thicker than the walls of the right ventricle.
C are the same thickness as the walls of the right ventricle. [1]

3 Match each blood vessel on the left to **two** statements on the right with straight lines.

Blood Vessel	Statements
Capillary	Has valves
	Smallest blood vessels
Artery	Thick muscular walls
	Small lumen
Vein	Thin permeable walls
	Large lumen

[6]

4 Name **three** substances carried by plasma. [3]

Total Marks .... / 17

Plants, Water and Minerals

1 Complete each statement below by naming the correct process.

   a) Minerals move into root hair cells by... [1]

   b) Water moves into root hair cells by... [1]

   c) Oxygen moves into the alveoli by... [1]

   d) Glucose moves from the intestine to the blood by... [1]

2 The guard cells to the right are found on the underside of a leaf.

What is their function? [2]

3 Transpiration is movement of water in a plant from roots to leaves.

For each of the following changes, state whether it will **increase** or **decrease** the rate of transpiration.

   a) Increase in wind velocity [1]

   b) Increase in temperature [1]

   c) Increase in humidity [1]

Total Marks .... / 9

Coordination and Control

You must be able to:

- Describe the structure of the nervous system
- Explain how the body produces a coordinated response
- Explain a reflex arc and its function.

The Nervous System

- The nervous system is composed of two parts:
  - the **central nervous system** – the brain and spinal cord
  - the **peripheral nervous system** – all the other nerve cells that connect to the central nervous system.
- The nervous system receives **stimuli** from the environment, via **receptors** in sense organs, and coordinates a response.

Sense Organs

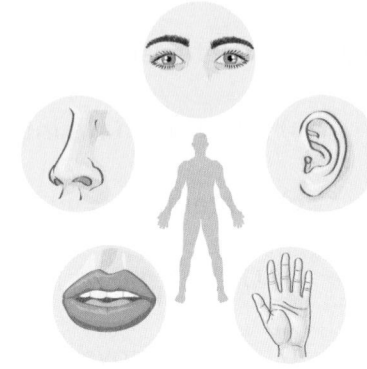

Neurones

- Messages are carried to different parts of the body as electrical impulses via **neurones**.

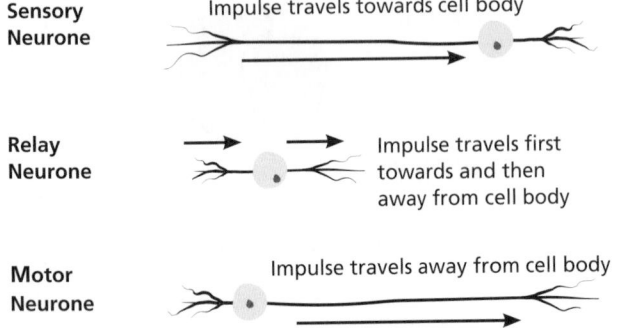

Sensory Neurone — Impulse travels towards cell body

Relay Neurone — Impulse travels first towards and then away from cell body

Motor Neurone — Impulse travels away from cell body

Sense Organ	Receptors Detect
Eye	Light
Ear	Sound
Nose	Smell
Tongue	Taste
Skin	Touch, pressure, pain, temperature change

- Sensory neurones carry impulses from receptors to the central nervous system.
- Relay neurones pass the impulse to a motor neurone.
- Motor neurones send the impulse to an **effector**, which is a muscle or gland that produces a response.
- The connection between two neurones is a gap called a **synapse**.
- When the impulse reaches the synapse, it stimulates the release of neurotransmitter chemicals from the neurone.
- The chemicals diffuse across the gap and bind to receptors on the next neurone.
- This triggers a new electrical impulse.
- At the synapse the message goes from electrical to chemical and back to electrical.

Chemical transmitter released here

A Synapse

Impulse

Neurone A

Receptor area

Cell body of neurone B

Electrical impulse generated in neurone B

Coordinated Responses

- In a voluntary (coordinated) response, there may be a number of possible responses.
- The impulse is sent to the brain, which makes a decision as to the best responses.

The Reflex Arc

- Reflexes are automatic responses to certain stimuli. You do not think about them.
- The function of a reflex is to protect the body.
- The response doesn't involve the brain – the pathway goes via the spinal cord, so it is quicker.
- A reflex response happens faster than a coordinated response. Example reflexes include touching a hot object, the pupil of the eye getting smaller in bright light and the 'knee jerk' reaction.

Touching a Hot Object

1. Receptors in hand detect pain.
2. Impulse sent via sensory neurone to central nervous system.
3. Impulse crosses synapse to relay neurone.
4. Impulse crosses synapse and is passed along motor neurone.
5. Response by effector muscle is to move hand away.

Pupil Reflex

Eye in Dim Light

Increased pupil size

Radial muscles contract

Circular muscles relax

Eye in Bright Light

Decreased pupil size

Radial muscles relax

Circular muscles contract

Quick Test

1. What are the **two** parts of the nervous system?
2. What is the function of a:
   a) sensory neurone?
   b) motor neurone?
   c) relay neurone?
3. What do the receptors detect in the:
   a) eye?
   b) ear?
4. Describe what happens at a synapse.

Key Words

central nervous system
peripheral nervous
 system
stimuli
receptor
neurone
effector
synapse

The Eye and the Brain

You must be able to:

- Identify the main parts of the eye and their function
- Describe some common defects of the eye and how they may be overcome
- Identify the areas of the brain and their functions
- **HT** Explain the difficulties and limitations of investigating brain function and treating damage and disease of the brain and nervous system.

The Eye

- The **cornea** is a transparent layer at the front of the eye.
- The **iris** is the coloured part of the eye. It opens and closes the pupil.
- The **pupil** is a hole that lets light into the eye.
- The **lens** focuses the light onto the retina.
- The **retina** changes light into electrical signals.
- The **optic nerve** sends the signals to the brain.
- The **ciliary body** and **suspensory ligaments** control the shape of the lens.
- The ciliary body also produces a liquid called aqueous humor.

Eye Defects

- Short sightedness is a defect where people cannot focus on objects far away. The image focuses in front of the retina.
- Short sightedness is corrected by using glasses with diverging or concave lenses.
- Long sightedness is a defect where people cannot focus on objects close up. The image is focused behind the retina.
- Long sightedness is corrected by using glasses with converging or convex lenses.

Normal Vision

 ◀Light

Long Sightedness

 ◀Light

Short Sightedness

 ◀Light

Colour Blindness

- Colour blindness is a deficiency in the way colour is seen.
- It is more common in men and is caused by a genetic defect on the X chromosome.
- The most common form of colour blindness is red–green blindness.
- There is currently no treatment for inherited colour blindness.

The Brain

- The cerebrum (the largest part of the brain, located in the front area of the skull) is composed of the two cerebral hemispheres that are divided into lobes.
- The outer layer, the cerebral cortex, is folded into ridges and furrows to increase its surface area.

 Key Point

The cornea works with the lens to focus the light.

The Eye

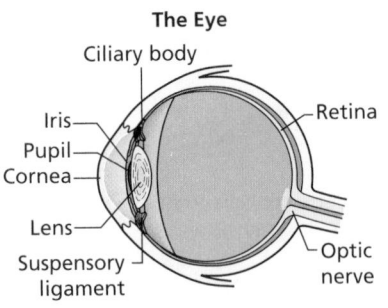

Ciliary body
Iris
Pupil
Cornea
Lens
Suspensory ligament
Retina
Optic nerve

 Key Point

Laser surgery can also be used to treat these defects.

 Key Point

Someone who is red–green colour blind may confuse a blue and purple pencil because they cannot see the red element of the purple pencil. To them the purple pencil appears blue.

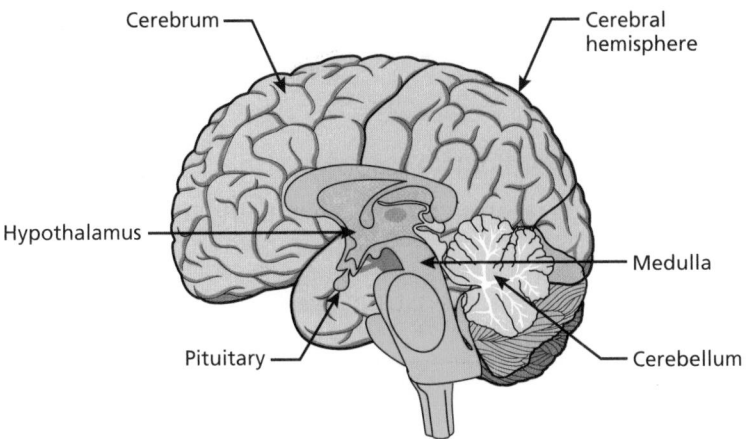

Labels: Cerebrum, Cerebral hemisphere, Hypothalamus, Medulla, Pituitary, Cerebellum

HT Investigating Brain Function

- Cognition (the mental act or process by which knowledge is acquired), attention and memory are complex processes that involve the entire brain.
- Therefore, it is vital that scientists experiment on the living brain if they are to find out how it works.
- Research can help in prevention and treatment of brain disease and help us understand how children learn.
- Brain activity can be measured by attaching microelectrodes to individual neurones within the brain or by using imaging techniques such as MRI (magnetic resonance imaging).
- There is a shortage of people with brain diseases and defects who are prepared to act as case studies for research.
- Some people may be unable to give their consent as a result of their condition.

HT Treating Disease and Damage

- While peripheral nervous tissue can regenerate to a limited extent, nervous tissue in the CNS cannot regenerate, i.e. if damaged, it cannot regrow.
- Surgery carries the risk that healthy areas of the brain or nervous system could be damaged.
- Delivering drugs to the central nervous system is challenging due to the selective permeability of the blood–brain barrier.

Key Words

cornea
iris
pupil
lens
retina
optic nerve
ciliary body
suspensory ligaments
HT blood–brain barrier

Quick Test

1. Which part of the eye:
   a) is where light is focused?
   b) opens and closes the pupil?
   c) send signals to the brain?
2. Explain the difference between short and long sightedness.
3. HT Suggest **two** reasons why brain damage is difficult to treat.

The Endocrine System

You must be able to:

- Describe how hormones can coordinate a response
- **HT** Explain negative feedback with reference to thyroxine and adrenaline production
- Describe the role of hormones in the menstrual cycle.

The Endocrine System

- Hormones are chemical messengers produced by glands.
- They are released directly into the blood and travel to the target organ.
- The cells of the target organ contain receptors to which the hormone can bind.

The Main Glands that Produce Hormones in the Human Body

- Pituitary gland
- Thyroid gland
- Pancreas
- Adrenal gland
- Ovary (female)
- Testes (male)

Gland	Hormone(s) Produced	Function / Target Organ
Pituitary	LH, FSH	Involved in reproduction
Pituitary	ADH	Controls water content of blood
Pituitary	Growth hormone	Stimulates growth
Thyroid	Thyroxine	Controls metabolism
Pancreas	Insulin and glucagon	Controls blood glucose levels
Adrenal	Adrenaline	Fight or flight
Ovaries	Oestrogen and progesterone	Reproduction and secondary sexual characteristics
Testes	Testosterone	Secondary sexual characteristics

HT Negative Feedback Systems

- Hormone production is often controlled by centres in the brain by the mechanism of negative feedback.
- Negative feedback mechanisms act like a thermostat in a home:
  - The temperature drops and the thermostat turns on the heating.
  - The thermostat detects the rise in temperature and turns off the heating.

Normal hormone levels — Drop in hormone levels — Increase hormone production — Reduce hormone production — Rise in hormone levels — Control centre in brain

HT Thyroxine

- Thyroxine is produced by the thyroid gland and regulates metabolism.
- The thyroid gland is controlled by the pituitary gland.
- When the level of thyroxine drops, the pituitary produces thyroid-stimulating hormone (TSH).
- TSH stimulates the thyroid gland to produce thyroxine.
- Increasing levels of thyroxine cause the production of TSH to decrease.
- Thyroxine levels return to normal.
- This is an example of negative feedback.
- Production of thyroxine negates the decreasing levels of thyroxine in the blood.

HT Adrenaline

- Adrenaline is called the 'fight or flight' hormone and is produced by the adrenal glands in response to exercise, anxiety or fear.
- Adrenaline increases heart and breathing rates, increases the rate of blood supply to the muscles and raises blood glucose levels in preparation for fight or flight.

> **HT Key Point**
>
> The pituitary gland is often called the 'master gland' because it controls several other glands.
>
> It produces TSH, which acts on the thyroid gland.
>
> It also produces adrenocorticotrophic hormone (ACTH), which acts on the adrenal glands.

Hormones in the Menstrual Cycle

- Three hormones each play a different role in the menstrual cycle.
- **Oestrogen** – causes build-up of the uterus wall.
- **Progesterone** – maintains the lining of the womb.
- **Follicle-stimulating hormone (FSH)** – stimulates release of an egg because it stimulates the ovaries to produce oestrogen.

The Menstrual Cycle

Ovary

Follicle with egg gradually develops

Ovulation (egg released)

Empty follicle gradually disappears

1. Uterus lining breaks down (i.e. a period).
2. Repair of the uterus wall. Oestrogen causes the uterus lining to gradually thicken.
3. Egg released by the ovary.
4. Progesterone and oestrogen make the lining stay thick, waiting for a fertilised egg.
5. No fertilised egg so cycle restarts.

Uterus wall rich in blood vessels

Thickness of Uterus Wall — Day of Cycle (0, 7, 14, 21, 28, 7)

> **Quick Test**
>
> 1. What hormone is secreted by:
>   a) the testes?
>   b) the thyroid gland?
> 2. Give **three** ways in which messages transmitted by hormones are different from messages transmitted by neurones.
> 3. How does FSH help to stimulate the release of an egg?

> **Key Words**
>
> gland
> **HT negative feedback**
> oestrogen
> progesterone
> follicle-stimulating hormone (FSH)

Hormones and Their Uses

You must be able to:

- Explain the use of hormones as contraceptives and their advantages and disadvantages
- HT Explain the interactions of hormones in the menstrual cycle
- HT Explain the use of hormones to treat infertility.

Hormones as Contraceptives

- Oestrogen can be used as a method of contraception.
- When taken daily, the high levels produced inhibit production of follicle-stimulating hormone (FSH) so egg development and production eventually stop.
- Progesterone also reduces fertility by causing a thick sticky mucus to be produced at the cervix, which prevents sperm from reaching the egg.
- There are over 15 methods of contraception.
- Hormonal contraceptives like the pill are very effective but can cause side effects and do not protect against sexually transmitted diseases (STDs)
- Barrier forms of contraception like condoms, may protect against STDs. They can be less reliable than hormonal methods if they are not used correctly.

> ### Key Point
>
> Most contraceptive pills combine progesterone and oestrogen.
>
> The progesterone-only pill is less effective.

	The Contraceptive Pill	Condoms
Advantage (High priority)	• More than 99% effective	• 98% effective • Protect against sexually transmitted diseases
Advantage (Low priority)	• Can reduce the risk of getting some types of cancer	
Disadvantage (High priority)	• Does not protect against sexually transmitted diseases	
Disadvantage (Low priority)	• Can have side effects	• Can only be used once

> ### Key Point
>
> You need to be able to evaluate risks and make decisions based on the evaluation of evidence. Decisions should always be justified.

When making a decision, divide the information into advantages and disadvantages and prioritise them.

HT Hormones in the Menstrual Cycle

- The hormones involved in the menstrual cycle interact with each other.
- FSH stimulates oestrogen production by the ovaries.
- Oestrogen causes the pituitary to produce luteinising hormone (LH) and to stop producing FSH.
- LH causes an egg to be released.

HT Treating Infertility

- Fertility drugs work by increasing levels of certain hormones in the body.
- If women have low levels of FSH, they can be given drugs containing FSH or LH to stimulate the release of eggs.
- Fertility drugs are also given to couples undergoing in vitro fertilisation (IVF) procedures to stimulate egg production.
- This allows several eggs to be collected at one time.
- The eggs are then fertilised outside the body.
- The cells divide to form an embryo, which is then inserted into the woman's uterus.

Scientific developments create issues

Social issues – the effect on people

Ethical issues – who has the right to decide which embryos 'live' or are destroyed

Economic issues – is the cost of developments worth the rewards?

Advances in IVF

New techniques offer the possibilities of improving a patient's odds of having a baby through in vitro fertilisation.

A single IVF cycle has about a 32% chance of resulting in a live birth and, to improve the odds, doctors often implant several embryos in the uterus during a single IVF cycle. This leads to high rates of twins and triplets, which can impact on the health of both mother and baby.

Chromosome abnormality is the main cause of miscarriage. Screening chromosomes involves taking cells from the embryo at day five to see if the normal number of chromosomes is present. Embryos with extra or missing chromosomes are not used. More research is needed on screening chromosomes, with a larger number of patients, to definitively determine the degree of benefit, especially since the cost of screening is around £2000 per patient.

Monitoring cell divisions is a technique that takes thousands of pictures of the embryos dividing at an early stage. If the division is atypical, the embryos are not used. Monitoring cell division has the advantage that it costs less and is less invasive.

Science has limititations

Science does not have an answer for everything – we still do not know enough about why the incidence of failure in IVF is so high.

There are also questions that science cannot answer, such as when is an embryo a person? Is destroying an embryo the same as taking a life? Different people will have different opinons.

Key Point

You need to evaluate the social, economic and ethical implications of scientific developments and understand the power and limitations of science.

Key Point

Scientific developments have the potential to improve the quality of life for many people but they also create issues.

Quick Test

1. What **two** hormones are commonly used in the contraceptive pill?
2. Suggest **two** advantages of using hormonal methods of contraception.
3. Suggest **two** disadvantages of using hormonal methods of contraception.
4. HT Explain how hormones can be used to treat infertility.
5. What do you understand by the terms social, economic and ethical?

Key Words

HT luteinising hormone (LH)

HT in vitro fertilisation (IVF)

HT embryo

Plant Hormones

You must be able to:

- Explain how auxins control growth in plants
- Describe the effects of plant hormones
- **HT** Describe the uses of plant hormones.

Auxins

- Auxins are hormones that affect the growth of plants.
- They change the rate of elongation in cells in the tips of plant roots and shoots:
  - In the shoot, auxins make the cells elongate more and promote growth.
  - In the root, they inhibit cell growth.
- **Phototropism** is the growth of a plant in response to light:
  - Auxin gathers on the shaded part of the shoot.
  - The auxin causes the cells to elongate.
  - The plant shoot bends towards the light.
- **Gravitropism** or **geotropism** is the response of the plant to gravity:
  - Auxin gathers on the lower side of the root due to gravity.
  - It inhibits cell growth.
  - The root grows in the direction of gravity.

> ### Key Point
>
> Shoots are positively phototropic and negatively geotropic. Roots are positively geotropic and negatively phototropic.

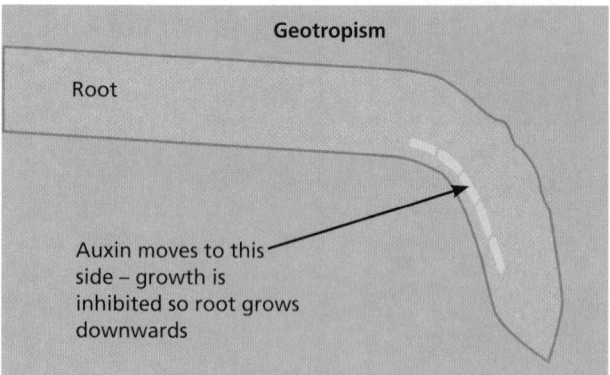

Geotropism

Root

Auxin moves to this side – growth is inhibited so root grows downwards

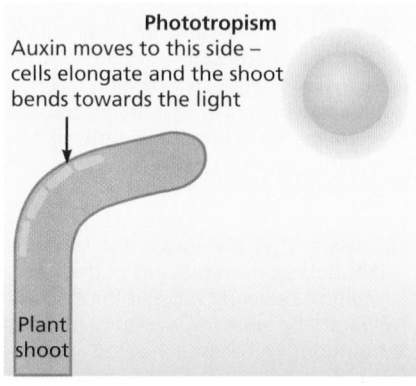

Phototropism

Auxin moves to this side – cells elongate and the shoot bends towards the light

Plant shoot

The Effects of Plant Hormones

- Auxin controls growth of plants in the shoots and roots.

- **HT** Gibberellin controls growth of the stem, promoting cell elongation between the nodes on the stem. It also delays the process of leaf shedding.
- **HT** Ethene promotes ripening of fruit and flower formation. It encourages plants to shed their leaves.

HT Uses of Plant Hormones

- Plant hormones can be extracted from plants and used in many applications.

WEED AWAY
Kills weeds, not grass

- Weed killers contain artificial auxin.
- They work by making the 'weed' grow too quickly, which results in it dying.
- Selective weed killers work on some plants but not others.
- Rooting powder contains auxins, which promote root development in cuttings.
- Some hormones called ethenes, can speed up the ripening of fruit.
- If plants are subjected to auxin in early ovule development, **parthenocarpic** fruit can be grown.
- Parthenocarpic fruit literally means *virgin fruit*. It is the natural or artificially induced production of fruit without fertilisation of ovules. The fruit is therefore seedless so has greater appeal. It also has a longer shelf life.
- Gibberlins can be used to stop dormancy and make seeds germinate at all times of the year.

Rooting hormone

A group of students wanted to find out if dwarf pea plants treated with plant hormone would develop into taller plants.

They treated five plants with plant hormone and compared them to a control group with no plant hormone.

The results are shown in the table.

Calculate the mean, mode and median of the results for the plants treated with plant hormone.

Results:

Height of Plant in cm (With Plant Hormone)	17	17	19	20	18
Height of Plant in cm (Control Group)	12	13	11	12	9

Mean:

$$\frac{17 + 17 + 19 + 20 + 18}{5} = 18.2$$

Mode:

17

Median:

17 17 **18** 19 20 = 18

> ### Key Point
>
> Remember – you need to be able to carry out statistical analysis.

The **average** height could be expressed as either the mean, median or mode.

Add up all results and divide by the number in the sample.

The number that occurs most frequently.

The middle number when they are ordered.

> ### Key Point
>
> From the results, you cannot conclude that gibberellins will cause all types of dwarf plants to develop into normal plants, only pea plants.

> ### Key Words
>
> phototropism
> gravitropism
> geotropism
> HT parthenocarpic
> mean
> mode
> median

> ### Quick Test
>
> 1. What is:
>   a) phototropism?
>   b) geotropism?
> 2. Explain how auxin affects the growth of shoots.
> 3. What effect does auxin have on plant roots?
> 4. HT Give **three** examples of how plant hormones can be used.

Maintaining Internal Environments

You must be able to:

- Explain why it is important to maintain a constant internal environment
- Describe the function of the skin in controlling body temperature
- Explain how blood sugar levels in the body are controlled
- Compare Type 1 and Type 2 diabetes.

Homeostasis

- **Homeostasis** means keeping the internal body environment constant.
- The body needs to control levels of water, glucose and salts to ensure chemicals can be transported effectively into and out of cells by osmosis and active transport.
- It also needs to maintain a constant temperature, since chemical reactions in the body are catalysed by enzymes that function best at their optimum temperature.

> **Key Point**
>
> Enzymes within the human body work best at 37°C.

The Skin

- The skin is an important organ in helping to control body temperature.
- The thermoregulatory centre in the brain detects changes in the temperature of the blood and coordinates a response by the skin.

Cross-Section Through Skin

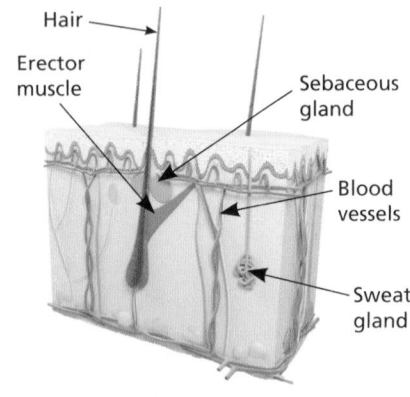

Hair — Erector muscle — Sebaceous gland — Blood vessels — Sweat gland

Core temperature too high
- Blood vessels in skin dilate (become wider) causing greater heat loss from the skin.
- Sweat glands release sweat (mainly water and salts) which evaporates, removing heat from the skin.
- Erector muscles cause hairs to lie flat and not trap heat.
- In hot and dry conditions, sebaceous glands produce oily sebum to encourage sweat to spread effectively.

Hypothalamus

Core temperature too low
- Blood vessels in skin constrict (become narrower) reducing heat loss from the skin.
- Muscles start to 'shiver', causing heat energy to be released via respiration in cells.
- Erector muscles cause hairs to stand up, trapping heat.
- In cool and wet conditions, sebaceous glands produce oily sebum that waterproofs the skin, helping excess water to run off.

- **Vasodilation** is when blood vessels become wider.
- **Vasoconstriction** is when blood vessels become narrower.

Control of Blood Sugar Levels

- Sugar in the blood comes from the food we eat.
- The blood sugar (glucose) levels are controlled by the pancreas.

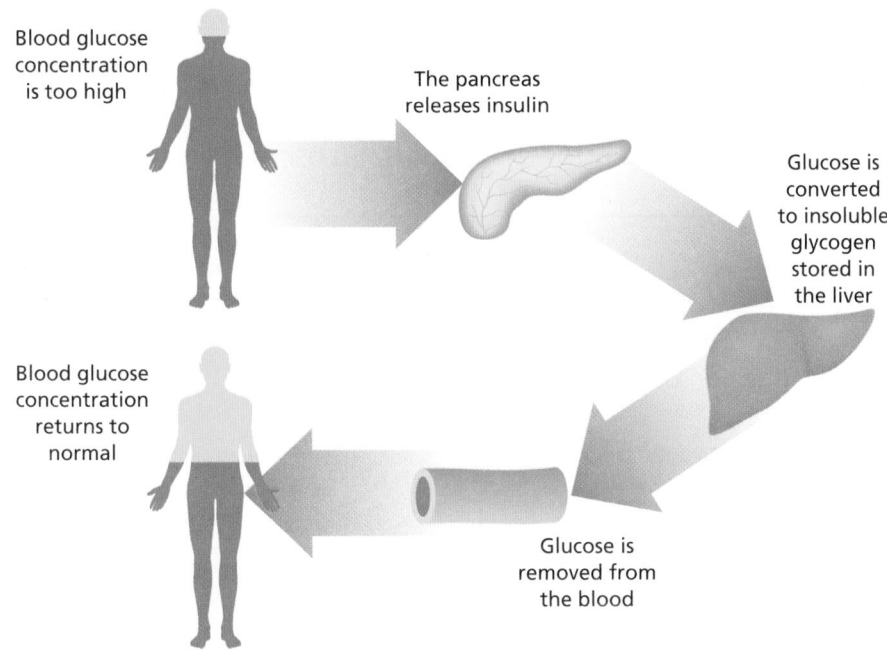

Blood glucose concentration is too high

The pancreas releases insulin

Glucose is converted to insoluble glycogen stored in the liver

Glucose is removed from the blood

Blood glucose concentration returns to normal

- The pancreas produces insulin which causes cells to become more permeable to glucose. Glucose moves from the blood into cells.
- Insulin also causes the liver to turn excess glucose into glycogen.

HT The pancreas also produces the hormone glucagon when blood glucose levels fall, e.g. during exercise.

HT Glucagon causes the liver to convert glycogen back into glucose and release it into the blood stream.

Diabetes

- Diabetes is a condition that causes a person's blood sugar level to become too high. There are two types of diabetes.

	Type 1	Type 2
Incidence	Less common	Most common
Onset	Develops suddenly, often at a young age	Develops gradually, often in people over 40 who may be overweight
Cause	Pancreas does not produce insulin	Not enough insulin is produced or cells are not affected by insulin
Treatment	Insulin injections for life, plus eating sensibly	Healthy eating, exercise, possible medication

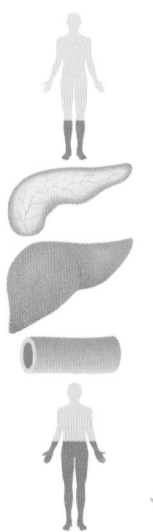

If the blood glucose concentration is too low…

the pancreas releases **glucagon**.

Insoluble glycogen from the liver is then converted to glucose…

which is released into the blood.

The blood glucose concentration returns to normal.

Key Words

homeostasis
vasodilation
vasoconstriction
pancreas
insulin
HT glucagon

Quick Test

1. Why is it important to maintain a constant body temperature?
2. How does the skin respond when we become too hot?
3. What effect does insulin have on the body?

Water and the Kidneys

You must be able to:

- Explain the effect of changing water potentials on the body's cells
- Describe the structure and function of the kidneys
- HT Describe the effect of ADH
- HT Explain the response of the body to temperature and osmotic changes.

Controlling Water Potential

- Water potential is a measure of the concentration of a solution.
- Water potential is affected by the concentration of dissolved ions in our body and also of the amount of water.
- Water moves by osmosis from an area of high water potential to an area of low water potential.

> **Key Point**
>
> Dilute solutions have higher water potential. Concentrated solutions have a lower water potential.

 1 **2** 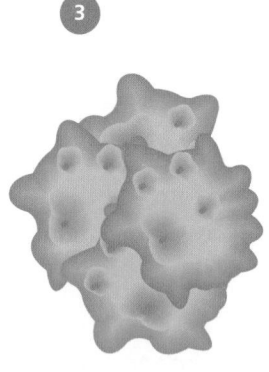 **3**

Ideal shape
A normal red blood cell.

Swollen
A red blood cell placed in a solution of high water potential. Water moves into the cell. The cell becomes swollen and will eventually burst. This is known as cell lysis.

Shrivelled
A red blood cell placed in a solution of low water potential. Water moves out of the cell and the cell shrinks. This is known as crenation.

> **Key Point**
>
> Lysis and crenation rarely happen inside the human body because the kidneys maintain the correct balance of water and ions.

- When the water level of plasma is low, the kidneys ensure the body retains water by producing less urine and more concentrated urine.
- When the water level of plasma is high, the kidneys ensure the body gets rid of water by producing large quantities of dilute urine.

The Kidneys

- The kidneys clean the blood by filtration.
- Each kidney is composed of about one million filtering units called nephrons.
- Blood entering the nephron is filtered at the glomerulus to produce glomerular filtrate.
- The filtrate passes into the tubules via the Bowman's capsule.
- As the filtrate passes through the tubules, all the glucose and some salts are reabsorbed. This is selective reabsorption.
- Excess salts and urea are excreted with water as urine.

Structure of the Nephron

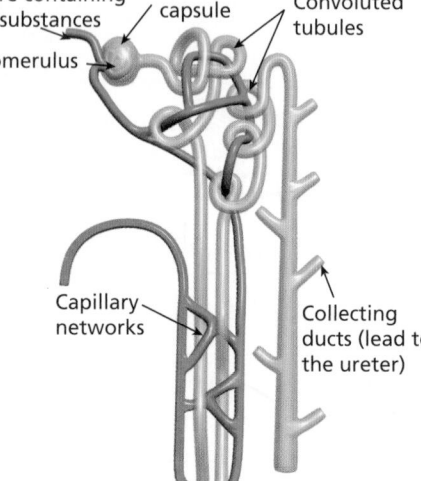

Blood under pressure containing waste substances

Bowman's capsule

Convoluted tubules

Glomerulus

Capillary networks

Collecting ducts (lead to the ureter)

Loop of Henlé

Kidney Tubules

Capillary   Tubule

Water
Ions
Urea
Sugar

Water
Ions
Sugar

Most of the water, ions and all sugar

Excess water, ions and all urea

1 Filtration

Lots of water plus all the small molecules are squeezed out of the blood, under pressure, into the tubules.

2 Selective reabsorption

The useful substances are reabsorbed into the blood from the tubules, and the amount of water in the blood is adjusted to maintain a constant level (osmoregulation).

3 Excretion of waste

Excess water, ions and all the urea now pass to the bladder in the form of urine and are eventually released from the body.

HT The Effect of ADH on the Kidneys

- Anti-diuretic hormone (ADH) alters the permeability of the kidney tubules.
- It is produced by the hypothalamus in response to a change in the water content of the blood.
- The body is able to respond to certain challenges:

Challenge	High sweating and dehydration	High ion intake	Excess water intake
Response	• Kidneys retain water and ions • Thirst mechanism activated	• Kidneys retain water and excrete more ions	• Kidneys produce more urine and retain ions

Effect of ADH – Another Example of Negative Feedback

Normal blood water level

Blood

High blood water level		Low blood water level

Hypothalamus

Receptors detect change		Receptors detect change

Pituitary gland

Less ADH secreted		More ADH secreted

Kidneys

Kidneys reabsorb less water		Kidneys reabsorb more water

Bladder

Large quantity of dilute urine produced		Small quantity of concentrated urine produced

Normal blood water level

Quick Test

1. What is the difference between high and low water potential?
2. When do the following conditions occur in red blood cells?
   a) Lysis
   b) Crenation
3. HT How does production of ADH affect urine output?

Key Words

lysis
crenation
nephron
tubule
selective reabsorption

Review Questions

Cell Structures

1 Draw a line from each cell part to the correct description.

Cell Part	Description
Cell membrane	Contains chlorophyll
Mitochondria	Gives support
Chloroplast	Controls movement of substances in and out of the cell
Cell wall	Contains the enzymes for respiration

[3]

Total Marks _____ / 3

What Happens in Cells

1 Explain what happens to an enzyme if the temperature is too high. [2]

2 Choose the correct word from each pair to complete the passage about enzymes.

Enzymes are **protein / carbohydrate** molecules. They are made up of **glucose / amino acid** chains.

They **slow down / speed up** the rate of reactions in the body and are **rejuvenated / denatured**

by high temperatures. The temperature that an enzyme works best at is called the

optimum / normal temperature. [5]

3 What are protein molecules made from?
Put a tick (✓) in the box next to the correct option.

Fatty acids	
Amino acids	
Carbolic acids	

[1]

4 Which of the **two** options below best describe a polymer.
Put a tick (✓) in the boxes next to the best answers.

A large molecule	
A small molecule	
A molecule made of repeating monomers	
A molecule made of different monomers	

[2]

5 Pectinase is an enzyme that catalyses the breakdown of pectin, a component of the cell wall in fruits. By breaking down the cell wall, pectinase releases the juice from within the cells.

A group of students wanted to investigate the effect of temperature on pectinase activity. They chopped an apple into small pieces and divided it into seven beakers.

They added pectinase to each beaker.

Each beaker was then placed into a different temperature water bath for 30 minutes.

After 30 minutes, the students filtered the apple–pectinase mixtures and collected the juice produced.

a) What is the independent variable in this experiment? [1]

b) What is the dependent variable? [1]

c) To make the test fair, suggest **two** variables the students should have controlled. [2]

The students recorded their results in a table

Temperature in °C	10	15	20	25	30	35	40
Amount of Juice Collected in cm³	5	7	9	12	16	17.5	15

d) Draw a graph of the students' results. [3]

e) What conclusions could the students draw from this experiment? [1]

f) Suggest **one** way in which the experiment could be improved. [1]

6 HT Protein synthesis involves the processes of transcription and translation.

Where in the cell do each of the processes occur? [2]

Total Marks .... / 21

Review Questions

Respiration

1 Tom is running up a hill.
Every few minutes he stops because he has to catch his breath by breathing deeply and his legs muscles feel painful.

a) What is the name of the substance that has built up in Tom's muscles and is causing pain? [1]

b) Why does Tom get out of breath? [4]

c) When Tom reaches the top of the hill he rests for 10 minutes and then begins to walk slowly back down.

i) What kind of respiration is occurring in Tom's cells as he starts his descent? [1]

ii) Write the equation for this type of respiration. [2]

iii) Where in the cell does this type of respiration occur? [1]

2 Steve wants to make some homemade strawberry wine.
He picks some strawberries and adds water and yeast to them.

a) What kind of microorganism is yeast? [1]

b) What substance does the yeast ferment to produce alcohol? [1]

c) After a few days, Steve notices that his wine is bubbling. Suggest why it is bubbling. [1]

Total Marks _____ / 12

Photosynthesis

1 Carol and Letisha are neighbours. They both have greenhouses in which they are growing lettuces.
Carol keeps her greenhouse warm using an electric heater.
Letisha uses a heater that burns paraffin, which is a fossil fuel.

a) Why do both Carol and Letisha heat their greenhouses? [2]

b) Letisha says she will get bigger lettuces because a paraffin heater is better for the plants than an electric heater.

Suggest why she says this. [2]

c) Apart from heating the greenhouses, what else could they do to increase the yield? [1]

d) Write the word equation for photosynthesis. [2]

e) How do the lettuces obtain the two reactants needed for photosynthesis? [2]

2 Some students wanted to carry out an experiment to investigate the effect of temperature on photosynthesis of pond weed.

The diagram shows the apparatus they used.

a) What are the names of the pieces of apparatus labelled **A** and **B**? [2]

b) Explain how the students could use the apparatus above to carry out their experiment. [2]

c) Name **two** pieces of equipment not shown in the diagram that the students would also need. [2]

d) HT The students notice that increasing the temperature from 30°C to 35°C does **not** result in more bubbles being produced.

Suggest why this is. [1]

3 Complete the sentences about photosynthesis by choosing the correct word from the list.

chloroplast   light   water   absorbs   oxygen   carbon dioxide   releases   chlorophyll

The green colour in plants is caused by a pigment called _____, which _____

light energy from the sun to use in photosynthesis. In addition to light, photosynthesis requires

_____, which is absorbed by the roots and _____, which enters the plants

through the leaf. [4]

4 Plants make their own food using photosynthesis.

Put a tick (✓) in the boxes next to the two reactants in photosynthesis. [2]

oxygen	
water	
glucose	
carbon dioxide	
nitrogen	
protein	

Total Marks _____ / 22

Review Questions

Supplying the Cell

1 Stem cells can differentiate into specialised cells.

  a) Identify the specialised cells below.

    A   B   C   D   E   [5]

  b) What is the function of cell **D**?   [1]

  c) What is the function of cell **E**?   [1]

  d) Explain how cell **E** is adapted for its function.   [4]

  e) Where are adult stem cells found?   [1]

2 Root hair cells absorb water from the soil.

How are root hair cells adapted for absorbing water?   [1]

3 The diagram below shows a working muscle cell

muscle cell

  a) Suggest what substance molecule **A** is most likely to be.   [1]

  b) What is the name of cell **B**?   [1]

  c) **C** is a blood vessel.

    Which of the following is **C** most likely to be?
    Put a tick (✓) in the box next to the best answer.

An artery	
A vein	
A capillary	

    [1]

4 Which of the following statements are true about stem cells in plants.
Put ticks (✓) in the boxes next to the correct answers.

Stem cells are found in meristematic tissues	
Stem cells are found in the tips of shoots and roots	
Stem cells do not have cell walls	
Stem cells are packed full of chloroplasts	

[2]

Total Marks	/ 18

The Challenges of Size

1 The pictures below show a unicellular organism called a *Paramecium* and a monkey, which is a multicellular organism.

Oxygen is able to pass into the *Paramecium* through the cell membrane.

a) By what process will this happen? [1]

b) Explain why the monkey has a specialised transport system that delivers oxygen to the lungs, but the *Paramecium* does not. [3]

Total Marks	/ 4

Review Questions

The Heart and Blood Cells

1 The diagram below shows two blood vessels.

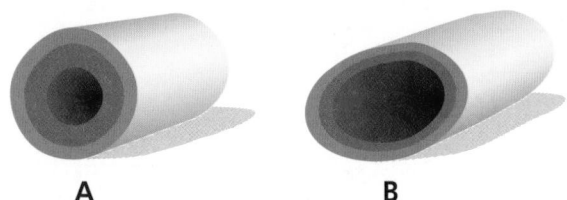

A   B

a) Which blood vessel will carry blood at high pressure? [1]

b) Which blood vessel has thick muscular walls? [1]

c) Which blood vessel has valves? [1]

d) Which blood vessel has the largest lumen? [1]

e) Draw an arrow on vessel **A** to show the lumen. Label it L. [1]

Total Marks .... / 5

Plants, Water and Minerals

1 A group of students wanted to investigate factors that affect water
loss in plants.
They took three plants, **A**, **B** and **C**.
They weighed each plant at the start of the experiment.
They covered the pot of plant **A** in a plastic bag and left it on a bench
in the shade.
They covered the pot of plant **B** in a plastic bag and left it in front of a fan.
They covered the pot of plant **C** in a plastic bag and left it on a sunny
window ledge.
After 24 hours the students reweighed each plant.

Shade

Fan

The students' results are shown in the table below.

	Plant A	Plant B	Plant C
Mass at Start (g)	400	420	410
Mass at End (g)	397	370	390
Change in Mass (g)			

Sunny ledge

a) Calculate the change in mass for each plant. [3]

b) Why did the students place plastic bags around the plant pots? [1]

c) Which plant lost the greatest mass? [1]

d) Suggest why it lost the greatest mass. [2]

2 Through which process do plants lose water?
Put a tick (✓) in the box next to the correct answer.

Translocation	
Transpiration	
Transfusion	

[1]

3 The diagram below shows a cross-section through the stem of a plant.

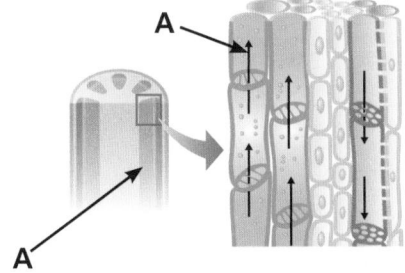

a) What is the name of the tubes labelled **A**? [1]

b) Name **one** substance transported in the tubes labelled **A**. [1]

c) Which statement below best describes the tubes labelled **A**?
Put a tick (✓) in the box next to the best answer.

Made of living cells with large channels in end walls	
Made of dead cells with end walls removed	
Made of living cells packed with mitochondria	

[1]

4 Minerals move from the soil into plants through the roots.

What is the name of the process by which minerals move into plant roots against a concentration gradient? [1]

Total Marks .... / 12

Practice Questions

Coordination and Control

1 Complete the table below about sense organs and the stimuli that they detect. [6]

Sense Organ	Stimulus Detected
Eye	**a)**
b)	Sound
Nose	**c)**
d)	Taste
Skin	**e)** and **f)**

2 The passage below is about nerve impulses. [4]

Choose the correct word from each pair.

Messages are carried by neurones as **electrical / chemical** impulses.

The junction between two neurones is called a **synapse / intersection**.

When the impulse reaches this junction, **hormones / neurotransmitters** are released.

These cross the gap and bind to **antigens / receptors** on the next neurone.

3 The diagram below shows the stages of a reflex arc.

What do **A**, **B** and **C** on the diagram represent? [3]

Stimulus → A → Sensory neurone → B

C ← Effector ← Motor neurone

Total Marks .... / 13

The Eye and the Brain

1 Draw a line from each part of the eye to its function. [3]

Part of Eye	Function
Pupil	Changes light into electrical signals
Lens	Hole that allows light to pass into eye
Retina	Focuses the light
Iris	Controls size of pupil

2 Which part of the eye carries the electrical impulses to the brain? [1]

3 The following questions are about the brain.

a) What is the function of the medulla? [1]

b) What is the function of the cerebellum? [1]

c) The surface of the brain is folded into ridges and furrows.

Explain why. [1]

4 HT Sarah cuts her finger and requires stitches.
Several weeks later the cut has healed.
Sarah's father has a stroke, which causes damage to some areas of the brain.

a) Explain why the damage caused to the brain does not heal. [1]

b) Sarah's father experiences loss of feeling in the right side of his body.

Suggest which side of the brain has been damaged by the stroke. [1]

Total Marks _____ / 9

Practice Questions

The Endocrine System

1 Match each gland to the hormone it produces by drawing a line between them.

Gland	Hormone
Thyroid	Insulin
Pancreas	Thyroxine
Testes	Testosterone
Pituitary	Anti-diuretic hormone

[3]

2 HT The paragraph below is about control of thyroxine levels.

Complete the paragraph choosing the correct words from the selection below.
You do **not** have to use all the words.

thyroid-stimulating hormone   **adrenaline**   **positive**   **glucose**
    metabolism   **thyroid**   **pituitary**   **negative**

Thyroxine is produced by the _____ gland. Its job is to control _____.

When levels of thyroxine in the blood fall, the decrease is detected by the _____

gland.

This gland produces the hormone _____, which causes an increase in production of

thyroxine. This is an example of _____ feedback.

[5]

Total Marks _____ / 8

Hormones and Their Uses

1 Oral contraceptives may contain oestrogen and progesterone, or progesterone on its own.

a) Give **one** disadvantage of the progesterone-only pill. [1]

b) How does progesterone help to prevent pregnancy? [1]

c) Where in the body are oestrogen and progesterone produced? [1]

d) Give **one** disadvantage of using oral contraceptives. [1]

Total Marks _____ / 4

Plant Hormones

1 Plants use hormones to respond to light and gravity.

   a) What is the name of the hormone that controls these responses? [1]

   b) Plant shoots are positively phototropic.

   What does this mean? [1]

   c) Roots grow in the direction of gravity.

   Why is this useful to the plant? [1]

2 A group of students carried out two experiments (A and B) to investigate the responses of plants to light.
In experiment **A**, the students shone a light from the side onto a growing shoot.
In experiment **B**, the tip of the shoot was covered with an opaque material.
The results are shown in the diagrams below.

What could the students conclude from these experiments? [1]

3 HT Plant hormones can be extracted from plants and used in a number of ways.

   Draw a line from each plant hormone to its use.

   Hormone   **Use**

Gibberellin		Ending seed dormancy
Auxin		Ripening fruit early
Ethene		Rooting powder

[2]

Total Marks _____ / 6

Practice Questions

Maintaining Internal Environments

1 The diagram below shows a cross-section of skin.

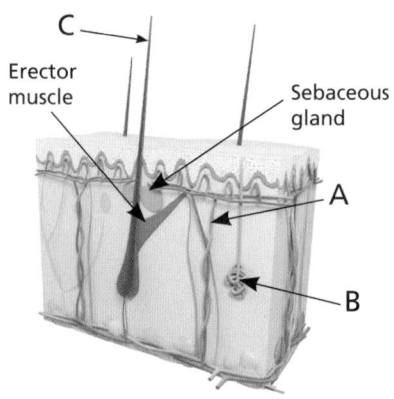

C

Erector
muscle

Sebaceous
gland

A

B

    a) What are structures **A**, **B** and **C**? [3]

    b) Explain what happens to each structure in hot temperatures. [3]

    c) Why is it necessary for humans to maintain a constant body temperature? [3]

2 Insulin increases the permeability of cells to glucose, so glucose can move from the blood into the cells.

    a) By what process does the glucose move from the blood into the cells? [1]

    b) For what process is the glucose required? [1]

3 HT Another chemical, glucagon, is involved in the control of blood glucose levels.

    Which of the following statements about glucagon are **true**?

    A Glucagon is a hormone.
    B Glucagon is produced by the liver.
    C Glucagon is an enzyme.
    D Glucagon is produced by the pancreas. [2]

Total Marks _____ / 13

Water and the Kidneys

1 The kidneys filter substances out of the blood.

    a) Name the **three** substances that are removed from the blood. [3]

    b) In which part of the nephron does selective reabsorption happen? [1]

2 Reabsorption of water in the kidneys is affected by a hormone.

    a) What is the name of this hormone? [1]

    b) Where is the hormone produced? [1]

    c) HT How does this hormone cause an increase in reabsorption of water? [1]

3 HT The hormone ADH is produced in the pituitary gland and released when osmosreceptors in the hypothalamus are stimulated.

Choose the correct answer to complete the sentence.

Osmoreceptors are likely to be stimulated the most by...

    A reduced blood pressure and low concentration of ions in plasma.
    B reduced blood pressure and high concentration of ions in plasma.
    C increased blood pressure and low concentration of ions in plasma.
    D increased blood pressure and high concentration of ions in plasma. [1]

Total Marks .... / 8

Recycling

You must be able to:

- Give examples of cycled materials and explain why cycling of materials is important
- Recall the key points in the carbon and nitrogen cycles
- Explain the role of microorganisms in cycling of materials.

The Importance of Recycling

- Living things are made of substances they take from the world around them.
- Plants take in elements such as carbon, oxygen, nitrogen and hydrogen from the air or from the soil.
- The plants turn the elements into complex carbohydrates, which are eaten by animals.
- These elements must be returned to the environment so they can be used by other plants and animals.
- Elements are recycled through biotic (living) components of an ecosystem (animals, plants, decomposers) and also abiotic (non-living) components (oceans, rivers, atmosphere).

The Water Cycle

- All living organisms need water to grow and survive.
- Water cycles through the atmosphere, soil, rivers, lakes and oceans.
- The water cycle is important to living organisms because it influences climate and maintains habitats.
- It also ensures there is flow of fresh water into lakes, rivers and the sea, and carries important nutrients.

The Nitrogen Cycle

- Nitrogen in the air must be turned into a form that plants can use by nitrogen fixation.
- Lightning 'fixes' nitrogen in the air and turns it into nitrates in the soil.
- Nitrogen-fixing bacteria in plant roots turn nitrogen into nitrates.
- The Haber process uses nitrogen to make fertilisers.
- Decomposition is the process by which dead animals and plants are turned into ammonium compounds by putrefying bacteria.
- Ammonium compounds are turned into nitrates by nitrifying bacteria.
- Denitrifying bacteria turn nitrates in the soil into nitrogen gas.

> **Key Point**
>
> Carbon, nitrogen and water are vital substances for all living things and must be recycled.

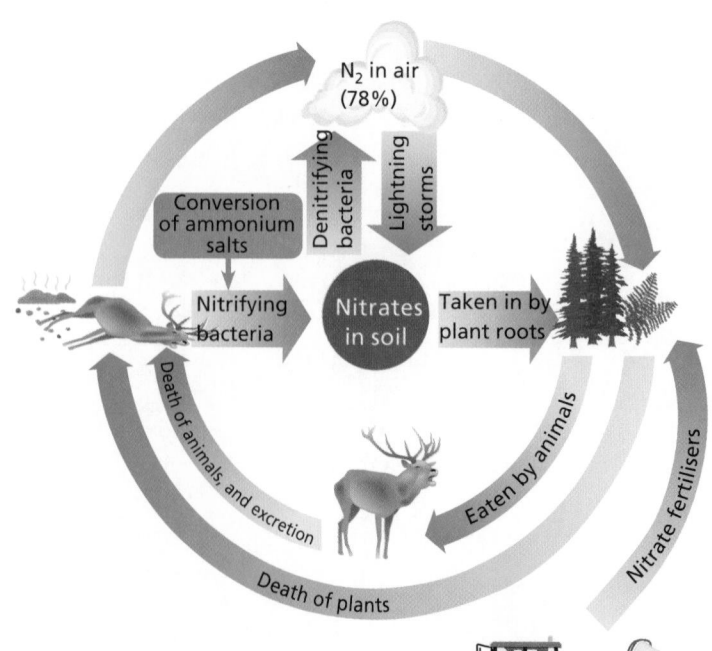

N_2 in air (78%)

Denitrifying bacteria

Lightning storms

Conversion of ammonium salts

Nitrifying bacteria

Nitrates in soil

Taken in by plant roots

Death of animals and excretion

Eaten by animals

Nitrate fertilisers

Death of plants

The Carbon Cycle

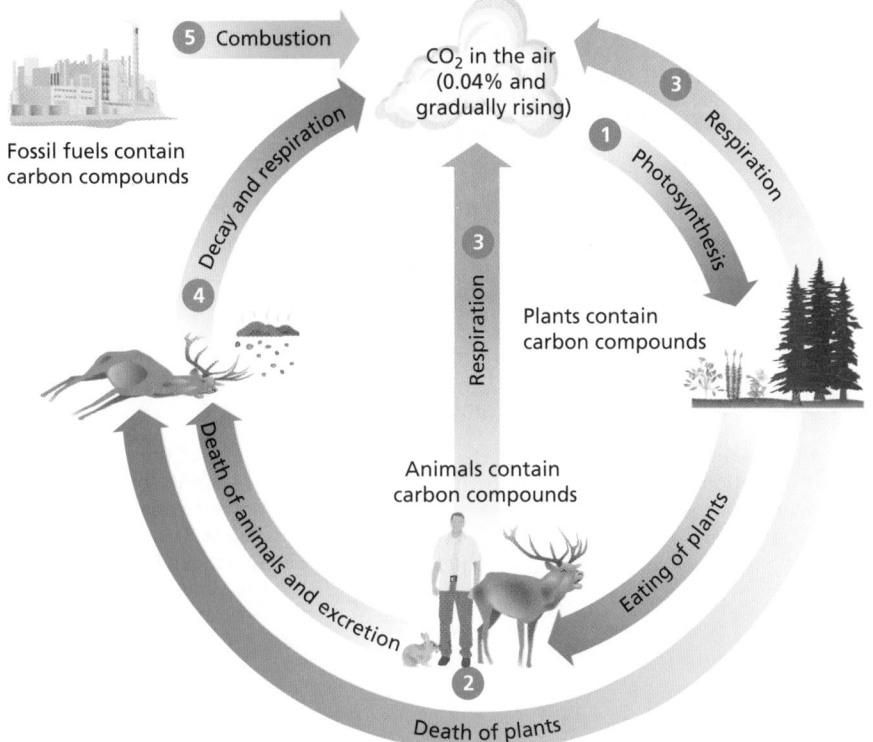

Combustion

CO_2 in the air (0.04% and gradually rising)

Fossil fuels contain carbon compounds

Decay and respiration

Respiration

Photosynthesis

Respiration

Plants contain carbon compounds

Animals contain carbon compounds

Death of animals and excretion

Eating of plants

Death of plants

1. Carbon dioxide is taken out of the atmosphere by plants when they photosynthesise.
2. The carbon in plants passes to animals when they are eaten.
3. Animals and plants respire releasing carbon dioxide back into the air.
4. Microorganisms **decompose** dead organisms and waste, and release carbon dioxide when they respire.
5. Combustion releases carbon dioxide into the atmosphere.

Key Point

Carbon dioxide is put back into the atmosphere by three types of respiration – animal, plant and microbial – along with combustion, and is removed by just photosynthesis.

Decay

- Microorganisms such as bacteria and fungi are called **decomposers**.
- They cause decay by releasing enzymes that break down compounds.
- They need water and a suitable temperature to survive.
- **Aerobic** bacteria also require oxygen to survive.
- Decay can happen in the absence of oxygen when caused by **anaerobic** bacteria.
- **Detritivores**, such as earthworms and woodlice, break down decaying material into small pieces, increasing its surface area and speeding up decay.

Quick Test

1. Name **two** types of decomposer.
2. Why is the water cycle important to living organisms?
3. Name the **four** types of bacteria that are involved in the nitrogen cycle.
4. How is carbon removed from the atmosphere?

Key Words

biotic
abiotic
nitrogen fixation
decompose
decomposers
aerobic
anaerobic
detritivores

Decomposition and Interdependence

You must be able to:

- Explain the effect of different factors on the rate of decomposition
- Describe the different levels of organisation in an ecosystem
- Explain how factors can affect communities
- Describe the importance of interdependence and competition in the community.

Decay

Experiment to Show Decay Caused by Microorganisms

1 Pour a solution containing nutrients into Flask A.

2 Melt and shape the neck of the flask.

3 Boil the nutrient solution to kill microorganisms and drive out air.

4 Seal the neck of the flask.

5 Pour more of the same nutrient solution into another flask (Flask B). Repeat stages 2–3, but this time snap the neck of the flask off.

Flask A

Flask A

Flask B

The experiment in the diagram above has been designed to test the following hypotheses:

i) Decay will only happen if microorganisms and oxygen are present (Flask B)

ii) Decay will not happen in the absence of microorganisms and oxygen (Flask A).

Both flasks should be filled with the same amount of nutrient solution and boiled for the same amount of time.

> You must use scientific explanations to develop hypotheses and plan experiments to test hypotheses.

- There are a number of factors that affect decay:

Factor	Effect	Reason
Oxygen	Lack of oxygen slows or stops decay.	Microorganisms are more active in aerobic conditions. Decay happens very slowly in anaerobic conditions.
Water	Lack of water slows or stops decay.	Water is needed to support chemical reactions in the decomposers.
Temperature	High temperatures slow or stop decay. Low temperatures slow decay.	The enzymes that cause decay are denatured at high temperatures. The rate of enzyme action is slower at low temperatures.

Levels of Organisation within an Ecosystem

- An ecosystem is a place or habitat together with all the plants and animals that live there.
- The plants and animals within an ecosystem form the **community**.
- A **population** is all the animals or plants of the same species within a community.

Word	Definition
Producer	All plants – they use the Sun's energy to produce food
Herbivore	An animal that eats only plants
Consumer	All animals – they consume food
Carnivore	An animal that eats only animals
Omnivore	An animal that eats both animals and plants
Trophic level	An animal's or plant's position in the food chain

Remember to use scientific vocabulary, terminology and definitions.

Producer — 1st trophic level

Primary consumer — Herbivore

Secondary consumer — Carnivore

Tertiary consumer — 4th trophic level

Omnivore

Factors Affecting Communities

- Biotic factors are living organisms or things that influence or affect ecosystems, for example:
  - number of predators
  - food availability
  - number of insects to pollinate plants
  - disease
  - human activity, such as mining, which may destroy habitats.
- Abiotic factors are non-living conditions or things that affect ecosystems and the organisms in them, for example:
  - temperature
  - light intensity
  - moisture levels
  - pH of soil
  - salinity (salt levels) of water.

Interdependence and Competition

- The organisms within a community may depend on other organisms for food (**predation**) or shelter.
- Sometimes an organism lives on another organism, e.g. mistletoe lives on trees and absorbs nutrients from the tree.
- This type of dependence is known as **parasitism**.
- **Mutualism** is a state in which two organisms depend on each other and both benefit, e.g. a bee feeds from a flower and the flower is pollinated.
- Organisms within a community will compete with each other:
  - animals compete for food, space, water, mates
  - plants compete for space, water, light, minerals.

Key Point

Mutualism benefits both organisms. Parasitism only benefits one organism and harms the other organism.

Quick Test

1. Name **three** factors that affect decay.
2. What happens to enzymes if the temperature is too high?
3. Suggest **two** biotic factors and **two** abiotic factors that affect a community.
4. Name **three** things for which animals may compete.

Key Words

community
population
predation
parasitism
mutualism

Biomass and Energy Transfers

You must be able to:

- Describe pyramids of biomass and explain how biomass is lost at each stage of the food chain
- Calculate the efficiency of energy transfers.

Food Chains and Biomass

- Food chains show what is eaten by what.
- Food chains also show the direction of energy flow.
- A food chain in a typical garden might be:

- In the food chain above, the leaf is eaten by the snail.
- Then the snail is eaten by the bird.
- Energy passes from the leaf to the snail to the bird.
- In a typical garden there may be thousands of leaves, hundreds of snails and a handful of birds.
- Biomass is the dry mass of living organisms.
- In the garden above, the biomass of all the leaves would be greater than the biomass of all the snails. The biomass of all the snails would be greater than that of all the birds.
- This can be represented by a pyramid of biomass:

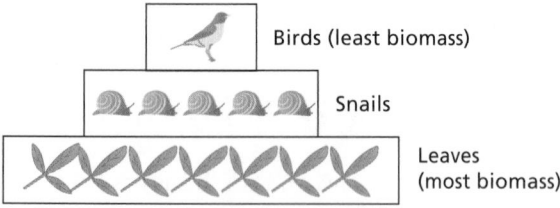

Birds (least biomass)

Snails

Leaves (most biomass)

Energy Loss

- As energy flows through the food chain, some energy is 'lost' at each stage:
  1. Organisms respire and move releasing energy.
  2. Warm blooded animals will release energy to keep them warm.
  3. Animals in the chain excrete and produce waste.
  4. Not all parts of the organism may be edible to the next animal in the chain, e.g. bones, shells or feathers.
- The energy available to each organism in the food chain decreases at each trophic level.
- Only 10% goes into making new cells in the next organism.
- Eventually there is not enough energy remaining to sustain another trophic level. For this reason food chains don't go on forever – they eventually run out of energy.

> **Key Point**
>
> In food chains → means 'eaten by'. The arrow always points to the consumer.

A Pyramid of Biomass with Four Trophic Levels

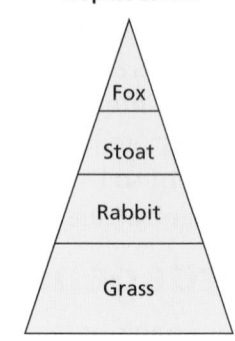

| Fox |
| Stoat |
| Rabbit |
| Grass |

> **Key Point**
>
> Food chains rarely have more than four trophic levels because energy is lost at each level.

Calculate the Efficiency of Energy Transfers

- The SI (Standard International) unit of energy is the joule (J).
- The efficiency of energy transfer from one organism to the next can be measured as a percentage:

$$\text{efficiency} = \frac{\text{energy transferred}}{\text{total energy available}} \times 100$$

In a field of grass, 25MJ of energy is available each year.

The rabbits eat the grass, but only have 2.5MJ of energy to pass on to the next level.

The stoats eat the rabbits and pass on 212 000kJ of energy each year to the foxes.

Calculate the efficiency of the energy transfer from:

a) the rabbits to the stoats

b) the stoats to the foxes

c) the grass to the foxes.

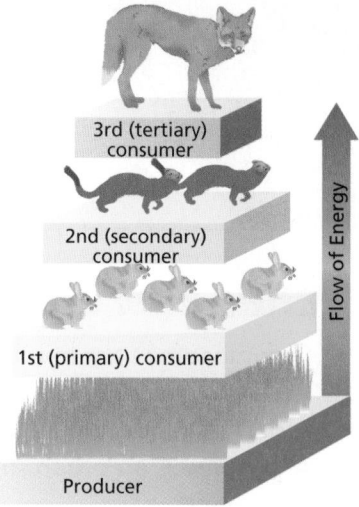

3rd (tertiary) consumer

2nd (secondary) consumer

1st (primary) consumer

Producer

Flow of Energy

$$\text{Grass} \xrightarrow{25MJ} \text{Rabbit} \xrightarrow{2.5MJ} \text{Stoat} \xrightarrow{212\,000kJ} \text{Fox}$$

> A simple diagram can help to make sense of the information you have been given.

a) Efficiency of transfer from rabbit to stoat $= \dfrac{2.5}{25} \times 100 = 10\%$

b) Energy in stoat = 2.5MJ or 2 500 000kJ.

> To calculate the energy efficiency of transfer from stoat to fox, the units for each must be the same.

Efficiency of transfer from stoat to fox $= \dfrac{212\,000}{2\,500\,000} \times 100$

$$= 8.48\%$$

> When faced with a long number with a lot of decimal places, round it off to a sensible number of decimal places.

c) Efficiency of transfer from grass to fox $= \dfrac{212\,000}{25\,000\,000} \times 100$

$$= 0.848\%$$

$$= 0.85\% \text{ (to 2 d.p.)}$$

> **Key Point**
>
> You must be able to interconvert units:
>
> 1 kilojoule (kJ) = 1000 joules
>
> 1 megajoule (MJ) = 1 million joules

Quick Test

1. Give **three** ways that energy is lost as it passes through a food chain.
2. Suggest why it would be unusual to find a food chain with six trophic levels.
3. What is the SI unit of measurement for energy?

> **Key Words**
>
> biomass
> joule
> efficiency

Genes

You must be able to:

- Explain the relationship between genes, chromosomes and the genome
- Describe how genes and the environment influence phenotype
- HT Describe how genetic variants influence phenotype.

Genes and Chromosomes

- **Chromosomes** are made of **DNA** and are found inside the nucleus.
- Each chromosome contains a number of **genes**.
- A gene is section of DNA that codes for a protein.
- A **genome** is an organism's complete set of DNA, including all of its genes.

Genotype and Phenotype

- Genes are responsible for our characteristics.
- We have two copies of every chromosome in our cells, therefore, we have two copies of each gene.
- The different forms of each gene are called **alleles**.
- We use capital and lower case letters to show if alleles are **dominant** or **recessive**.
- If two dominant alleles are present, e.g. BB, the dominant characteristic is seen, e.g. brown eyes.
- If two recessive alleles are present, e.g. bb, the recessive characteristic is seen, e.g. blue eyes.
- If one of each allele is present, e.g. Bb, the dominant character is seen, e.g. brown eyes.
- In the case of eye colour for example, brown eyes are dominant and would be shown as BB or Bb.
- Blue eyes on the other hand, are recessive and would be shown as bb.
- The **phenotype** is the characteristic that is seen, e.g. blue eyes.
- The **genotype** is the genes that are present, e.g. bb.

A Cell

Chromosomes

A Section of Chromosome

 ← A gene

A Section of DNA

A Section of Uncoiled DNA

	A person who is **heterozygous** has two different alleles.	A person who is **homozygous** has both alleles the same.
Genes on Chromosomes		
Alleles	One allele for blue eyes, one for brown eyes	Both alleles are for blue eyes
Heterozygous or Homozygous	Heterozygous	Homozygous
Genotype	Bb	bb
Phenotype	Brown eyes	Blue eyes

> ### Key Point
>
> Capital letters represent dominant alleles.
>
> Lower case letters represent recessive alleles.

> ### Key Point
>
> A human body cell has 46 chromosomes, arranged in 23 pairs.

Environment and Phenotype

- Inherited variation is caused by the genes inherited from parents.
- Environmental variation is caused by environmental factors, e.g. diet.
- The phenotype of an organism is often the result of both genetic and environmental variation.
- For example:
  - a person who inherits light skin may, through prolonged exposure to the sun, develop darker skin
  - a person who inherits 'tall' genes may not grow tall if poorly nourished.
- Some characteristics show continuous variation, for example height. A person can be tall or short or anywhere in between the two.
- Characteristics that show discontinuous variation have a limited number of possible values. For example, blood groups are either A, B, AB or O.

Characteristics Controlled Solely by Inheritance	Factors that are Influenced by Environment and Inheritance
Eye colour	Height and weight
Hair colour	Intelligence
Blood group	Artistic or sporting ability
Inherited diseases	Skin colour

HT Mutations and Phenotype

- Sometimes, when DNA is copied, it results in a mutation or genetic variant. Often this mutation has no effect on phenotype.
- If the mutation happens in coding DNA, it can affect the structure of proteins made.
- The protein may:
  - continue to function normally
  - have reduced function
  - lose its function completely.
- In enzymes, the active site may no longer fit the substrate.
- In humans, about 98% of DNA does not code for protein production.
- Some of this DNA controls whether a gene is expressed by turning gene transcription on or off.
- If a mutation happens in non-coding DNA it may alter how genes are expressed.

Normal Gene **Mutated Gene**

The G base is substituted for an A base

Key Words

chromosome
DNA
gene
genome
allele
dominant
recessive
phenotype
genotype
heterozygous
homozygous
continuous
discontinuous
HT variant

Quick Test

1. What is a genome?
2. How do we show whether an allele is dominant or recessive?
3. Suggest **two** characteristics that may be affected by the environment.
4. Give an example of:
   a) continuous variation
   b) discontinuous variation.

Genetics and Reproduction

You must be able to:

- Explain advantages and disadvantages of sexual and asexual reproduction
- Describe meiosis and explain its role in genetic variation
- Use genetic crosses to determine the outcomes for sex and other characteristics
- Describe the work of Mendel in developing our understanding of genetics.

Sexual and Asexual Reproduction

Type of Reproduction / Features	Sexual	Asexual
Gametes (sex cells)	Involves fusion of two gametes	Gametes not involved
Parents	Two parents	One parent
Variation	Produces variation in offspring (this is important in the process of natural selection)	No variation – offspring are clones of parent (a possible disadvantage since the whole population could be susceptible to an environmental pressure)
Where it is found	Method of reproduction in most animals and plants	Bacteria, some plants and a small number of animals, e.g. starfish
Numbers of offspring	Number limited per birth	Can produce many offspring rapidly, which is an advantage

Meiosis

- Meiosis is a type of cell division that produces gametes.
- The cell divides twice to produce four gametes with genetically different sets of chromosomes.
- Gametes have half the number of chromosomes as body cells. This is called a haploid number.

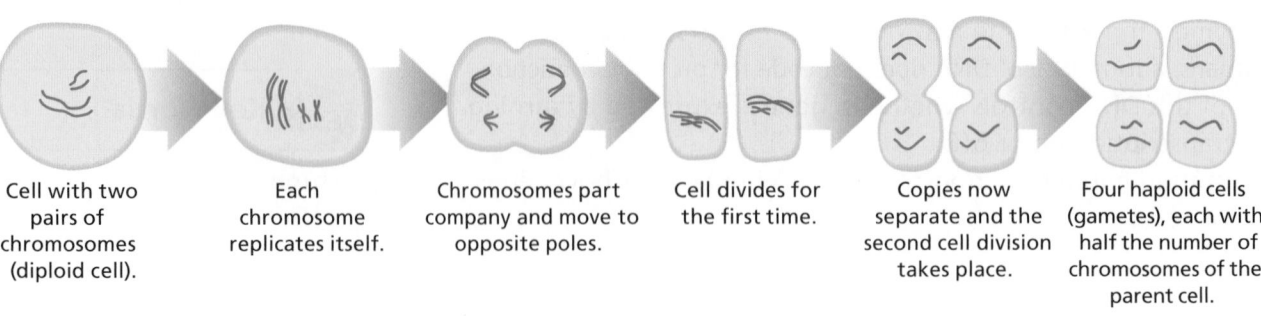

Cell with two pairs of chromosomes (diploid cell). → Each chromosome replicates itself. → Chromosomes part company and move to opposite poles. → Cell divides for the first time. → Copies now separate and the second cell division takes place. → Four haploid cells (gametes), each with half the number of chromosomes of the parent cell.

- When the gametes fuse in fertilisation, the normal diploid number of chromosomes is restored.
- Fusion of gametes is a source of genetic variation.

Determination of Sex

- Sex inheritance is controlled by a whole chromosome rather than a gene.
- In humans, the 23rd pair of chromosomes in males contains an X and a Y chromosome; females have two X chromosomes.

> **Key Point**
>
> The chance of having a male child is always 50%, as is the chance of having a female child.

Genetic Crosses

- A genetic cross looks at the possible outcomes for offspring with parents of the same or different genotypes.
- All the offspring of a cross between a homozygous dominant and a homozygous recessive will appear to have the dominant characteristic.
- A cross between two heterozygous parents will give a ratio of three offspring with the dominant characteristic to one with the recessive.

The Work of Mendel

- Gregor Mendel was a monk who spent many years researching inheritance in pea plants.
- He found that flowers were either purple or white with no intermediate colours.
- This challenged the hypotheses of other scientists who thought that inherited traits blend from one generation to the next.
- By doing thousands of experiments on pea plants, Mendel came up with three important conclusions:
  - Inheritance is determined by 'units'.
  - An individual inherits one 'unit' from each parent for each trait.
  - A trait may not show up in an individual but can be passed on.
- Mendel's 'units' are what we now know as genes.
- The principles he discovered for plants are essentially the same for most living things.

Key Point

Most of the characteristics we exhibit are not controlled by a single gene, but are the result of multiple gene inheritance.

Key Point

Scientists come up with a hypothesis and gather evidence. If the evidence supports the hypothesis, it is accepted until someone offers a better hypothesis and new evidence.

Quick Test

1. What is the difference between a haploid cell and a diploid cell? Give an example of each.
2. Give **three** differences between sexual and asexual reproduction.
3. Explain why there is a 50/50 chance of having a male or female baby.

Key Words

gamete
haploid
diploid

Natural Selection and Evolution

You must be able to:

- Understand there is extensive genetic variation within a population and relate this to evolution
- Describe the evidence for evolution and the work of Darwin and Wallace
- Explain how the development of ideas on evolution have impacted on modern biology, including the impact on classification systems.

Darwin's Theory of Evolution

- Evolution is the gradual change in the inherited characteristics of a population over a large number of generations, which may result in the formation of a new species.
- Charles Darwin's theory of evolution suggested:
  - There is much variation within a species.
  - There is a struggle for survival and organisms have more offspring than can survive.
  - Those that are best adapted to their environment are likely to survive, breed and pass on their genes to the next generation (survival of the fittest).
  - Those that are least well adapted are likely to die.
- Another scientist called Alfred Wallace carried out similar research at the same time and supported Darwin's ideas about evolution.
- Darwin's theory was not accepted until after his death because there was not enough evidence (genes and the mechanism of inheritance had not been discovered).
- His ideas were not popular at the time because they contradicted the belief that God had created all life on Earth.
- There is still some debate among scientists today about how life began.
- The work of Darwin and Wallace had a profound impact on society at the time and continues to shape scientific understanding.
- At the time it created great controversy, but it also created a new line of thought.

Mutations

- Variation can arise because of mutations in a gene.
- If the mutation results in a characteristic that gives the organism an advantage over organisms without the characteristic, it is more likely to survive, breed and pass on the mutated gene to its offspring.

Using Darwin's idea of survival of the fittest, you might hypothesise:

'Animals that are better camouflaged are less likely to be seen by predators.'

A model can be used to test this hypothesis using blue, green, red and brown strands of wool:

Key Point

Scientific models are used to explain and predict the behaviour of real objects or systems that are difficult to observe directly.

- Thirty 5cm strands of each colour of wool are scattered randomly in a field.
- A group of students are given 1 minute to find as many strands as they can.

Using the model, you might predict that:

- More red and blue strands of wool will be found because they are not camouflaged.
- Fewer green and brown strands will be found because they are better camouflaged.

Evidence for Evolution

- The fossil record gives us evidence of change over a long period of time, however there are gaps in this record.
- **Antibiotic resistance** provides evidence for evolution – bacteria divide very rapidly, so evolution by natural selection can be seen in a very short period of time:
    - A mutation may cause a bacterium to be resistant to an antibiotic.
    - Most of the bacteria in the population are killed by the antibiotic.
    - The antibiotic-resistant bacteria multiply rapidly to form a colony of resistant bacteria.

Developments in Classification Systems

- Developments in biology have had a significant impact on classification systems.
- The binomial classification system places organisms into groups based on a large number of characteristics such as anatomy, physiology, biochemistry and reproduction.
- This helps us to understand how organisms are related to each other.
- Darwin's theory of evolution provided a new explanation for how to group organisms:
    - nearness of descent
    - phylogeny (the sequence of events involved in the evolution of a species).
- **Phylogenetic** systems of classification help us understand the evolutionary history of organisms:
    - DNA sequencing can be used to show if organisms share common ancestors.
    - DNA sequencing has led to some organisms being reclassified.

Natural Classification of Sumatran Orang-utan

Level	Example
Kingdom	Animalia
Phylum	Chordata
Class	Mammalia
Order	Primates
Family	Hominidae
Genus	*Pongo*
Species	*Pongo abelii*

The Bornean orang-utan, *Pongo pygmaeus*, shares the same genus, which shows they are closely related. They developed as two separate species following the separation of Borneo and Sumatra.

Phylogenetic Tree

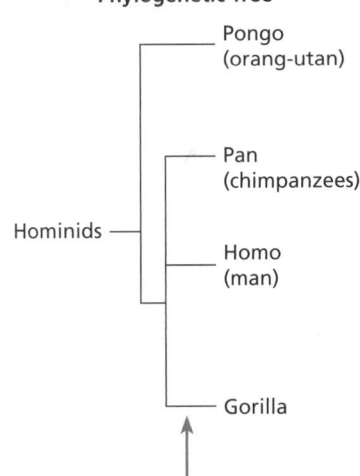

This shows that man, chimps, gorillas and orang-utans all share a common ancestor. It is thought that man is more closely related to gorillas than orang-utans.

Quick Test

1. Explain Darwin's theory of natural selection.
2. Explain how antibiotic resistance develops.
3. How does DNA sequencing help to classify organisms?

Key Words

mutation
antibiotic resistance
phylogenetic

Coordination and Control

1 Bryn runs into the road without looking.
There is a car coming towards him.
The driver of the car has to brake suddenly.

    a) What sense organ does the driver use to see Bryn? [1]

    b) Was braking a reflex action or a voluntary response for the driver? [1]

    c) The response was to push down on the brake pedal – what was the effector that carried out the response? [1]

2 The diagram below shows a neurone.

    a) What type of neurone is shown? [1]

    b) Put an arrow on the diagram to show the direction of an impulse through the neurone. [1]

3 The bar chart below shows the average speed of nerve impulses in different animals.

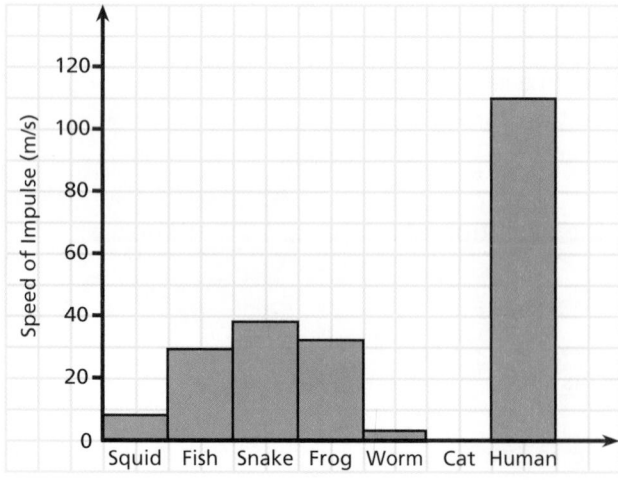

    a) The average speed of an impulse in cats is 90 metres per second. Plot this on the chart. [1]

    b) Impulses travel faster at higher temperatures.

        What evidence is there from the chart to support this? [2]

Total Marks _____ / 8

The Eye and the Brain

1 The diagram below shows an eye.

a) Which letter shows the retina? [1]

b) Which letter shows the lens? [1]

c) What is the name of the part labelled D? [1]

d) What is the function of the part labelled B? [1]

e) How can you tell from the diagram that this person is neither short- nor long-sighted? [1]

f) Someone who is long-sighted cannot focus on objects near to them.
They can be given glasses to correct the defect.

What kind of lenses would be used in the glasses? [1]

> **Total Marks** .... / 6

Review Questions

The Endocrine System

1 The graph to the right shows the chance of a woman conceiving a baby naturally at different ages.

a) Between what ages is there a significant drop in the chances of conceiving? [1]

b) Use the graph to predict the chance of a woman aged 37 conceiving. [1]

c) **HT** Women who have difficulty conceiving may be given hormone treatments to stimulate the release of eggs.

   i) Which hormones are commonly present in these drugs? [2]

   ii) Suggest why a woman aged over 45 is unlikely to be offered such treatment. [1]

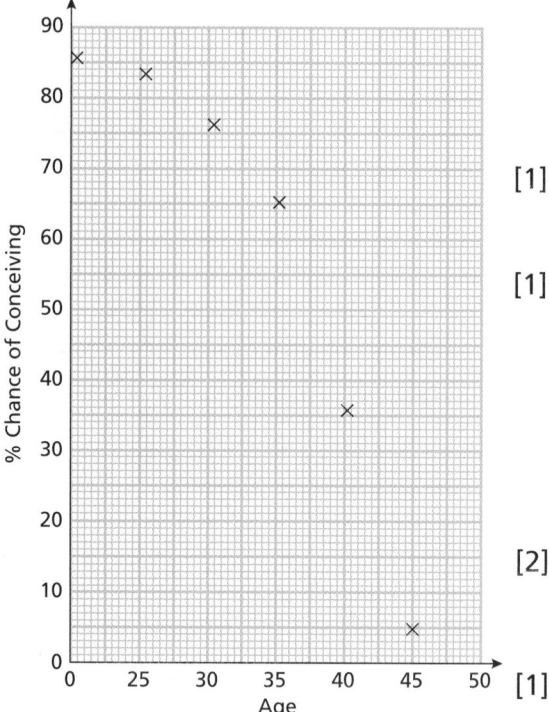

2 The diagram below shows how the thickness of the lining of the womb changes during the menstrual cycle.

Oestrogen causes the lining of the womb to thicken.

Which of the following statements best describes how oestrogen levels change? Put a tick (✓) in the box next to the best answer.

Oestrogen levels will increase from day 14 to day 21.	
Oestrogen levels will increase from day 0 to day 2.	
Oestrogen levels will increase from day 2 to day 14.	

[1]

3 The diagram below shows several organs that produce hormones.

a) What is the name of **A**? [1]

b) What hormone is produced by **B**? [1]

c) Which letter shows where adrenaline is produced? [1]

d) What is the name of the male sex hormone produced at **D**? [1]

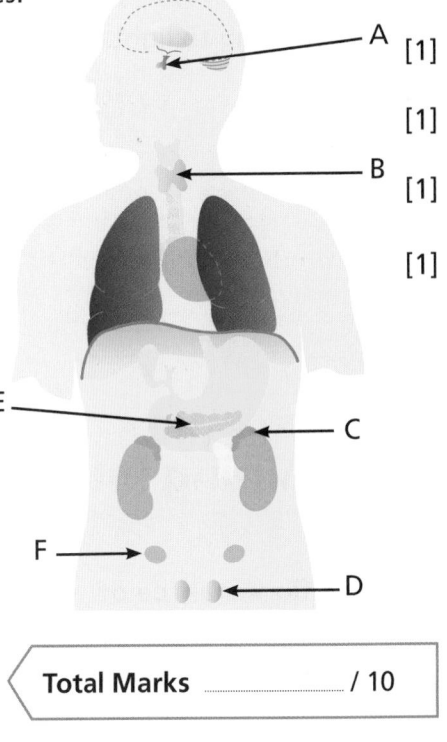

Total Marks _____ / 10

Hormones and Their Uses

1 Complete the passage below about oral contraceptives by choosing the correct words from the list. You do **not** have to use all the words.

side effects　　**sexually transmitted diseases**　　**FSH**　　**more**
less　　**oestrogen**　　**progesterone**

Oral contraceptives are taken to prevent pregnancy. The combined pill contains the hormones

_____ and _____. It is _____ reliable than the progesterone-

only pill. One of the disadvantages of using the contraceptive pill is it can cause _____. [4]

Total Marks _____ / 4

Plant Hormones

1 Complete the sentences below about plant hormones by choosing the correct word from each pair.

Auxin is a plant hormone that controls plant **growth / germination**.

In **roots / shoots**, auxin encourages cells to elongate.

In **roots / shoots**, auxin inhibits growth of cells.

Auxin is responsible for a plant's response to **temperature / light**. [4]

Review Questions

2 Explain as fully as you can what is happening in the diagram, which shows a plant responding to light. [3]

Light source

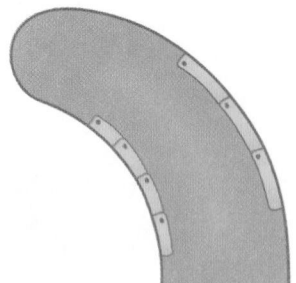

Total Marks _____ / 7

Maintaining Internal Environments

1 The flow chart below shows the control of blood glucose levels by the hormone insulin.

Glucose enters blood from small intestine
↓
Blood glucose levels rise
↓
Pancreas releases insulin into the blood
↓
↓
↓
Blood glucose levels return to normal

a) By what process is glucose absorbed into the blood? [1]

b) Complete the fourth and fifth level in the flow chart. [2]

c) **HT** During exercise, blood glucose levels may drop.

i) Why might glucose levels drop? [2]

ii) Explain how the body responds to the drop in glucose levels. [4]

2 Hormones play an important part in regulating the body's internal conditions.

    a) What term is given to organs that produce hormones? [1]

    b) How do hormones travel to their site of action? [1]

> **Total Marks** _____ / 11

Water and the Kidneys

1 Gavin is playing football on a hot day. He is getting very hot.

    a) How does Gavin's skin help him to cool down? [3]

    b) Gavin drinks plenty of water during the game.

       Which organ in the body controls water balance? [1]

2 The table below shows how the volume of sweat and urine changes with the outside temperature.

Temperature (°C)	0	5	10	15	20	25	30
Volume of Urine Produced per Hour (cm³)	100	92	85	78	68	58	46
Volume of Sweat Produced per Hour (cm³)	0	2	5	10	20	50	90

    a) Describe how the amount of sweat produced changes as the temperature increases. [3]

    b) How does sweating cool the body? [1]

    c) Describe the relationship between the amount of sweat and amount of urine produced. [1]

    d) In which part of the nephron are ions reabsorbed? [1]

    e) HT ADH is the hormone responsible for controlling the water content of the body.

       Describe the effect of increasing levels of ADH on the kidney. [2]

    f) HT Alcohol suppresses ADH production.

       Why is it **not** sensible for someone to drink alcohol to keep cool on a very hot, sunny day? [2]

> **Total Marks** _____ / 14

Practice Questions

Recycling

1 The processes below are about the nitrogen cycle.

Match each process to the type of bacteria that are involved in it by drawing a line between them.

Process | **Type of Bacteria**

Process	Type of Bacteria
Nitrogen gas turned into nitrates by bacteria in plant roots	denitrifying
Animal and plant material and waste products turned into ammonium compounds	putrefying
Ammonium compounds turned into nitrates	nitrogen-fixing
Nitrates turned into nitrogen gas	nitrifying

[3]

2 The diagram below shows the carbon cycle.

a) What letter represents each of the following processes?

   i) Photosynthesis

   ii) Animal respiration

   iii) Consumption

   iv) Microbial respiration

   v) Plant respiration   [5]

CO_2 in air (0.04%)

b) What process is shown by the letter **B**?   [1]

c) Name a process, **not** shown on the diagram, that releases carbon dioxide into the atmosphere.   [1]

Total Marks .... / 10

Decomposition and Interdependence

1 Choose the correct statement from the sentences below, which are about decay.

    A Decay happens faster when it is cold and moist.

    B Decay happens faster when it is warm and moist.

    C Decay happens faster when it is cold and dry.

    D Decay happens faster when it is warm and dry. [1]

2 The diagram below shows a woodland food chain.

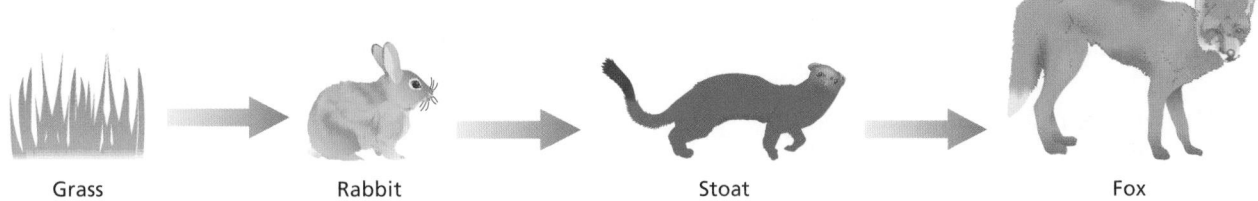

Grass   Rabbit   Stoat   Fox

  a) In the food chain, name:

    i) a predator [1]

    ii) a producer [1]

    iii) the secondary consumer. [1]

  b) Which animal occupies the second trophic level? [1]

  c) Draw a pyramid of biomass for the food chain. [2]

  d) What is the name used to describe all the animals and plants in this habitat? [1]

3 Divide the words below into **biotic** and **abiotic** components of an ecosystem.

animals   **bacteria**   **rivers**   **trees**   **soil**   **sea**   **detritivores** [7]

Practice Questions

4 In the Scottish island of Orkney, voles are eaten by birds of prey called hen harriers. Voles are also eaten by owls.

a) Name **two** organisms that are in competition with each other for food.   [1]

b) What is the relationship between vole and owl?   [1]

c) Several years ago, stoats were introduced to the island. Stoats also eat voles. Local conservation groups are worried that the stoat numbers are growing rapidly.

How is rapid growth of the stoat population likely to affect the numbers of hen harriers? Give a reason for your answer.   [2]

d) Suggest a factor, other than food, that two of the organisms may be in competition for.   [1]

5 The diagram shows a food web.

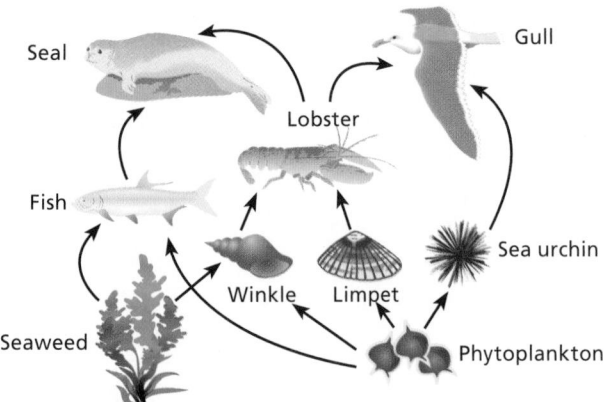

a) Name a producer in the food web.   [1]

b) Name a top predator.   [1]

c) Name an organism that occupies the second trophic level.   [1]

d) Name **two** organisms that are in competition with each other for food.   [1]

6 Some students noticed that the grass growing in one part of the school field was longer and greener than grass growing in another area.

Suggest **three** factors that may be affecting the growth of the grass.   [3]

> **Total Marks** _____ / 27

Biomass and Energy Transfers

1 Which of the following best describes biomass?

    A The amount of energy in a habitat.

    B The number of animals in a food chain.

    C The amount of living material. [1]

2 The diagram shows a pyramid of numbers for an area of farmland.

Hawk
Thrushes
Slugs
Lettuce

    a) Name the producer. [1]

    b) Name the secondary consumer. [1]

    c) Construct a pyramid of biomass for the four organisms. [2]

3 The diagram below shows the flow of energy in a food chain from plants to caterpillars to birds.

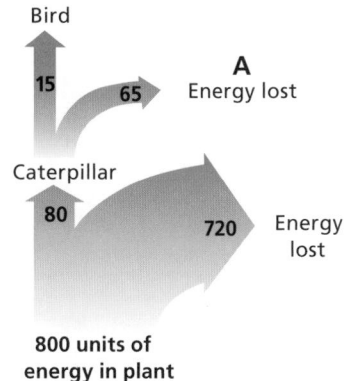

Bird
15
65 → **A** Energy lost

Caterpillar
80
720 → Energy lost

800 units of energy in plant

    a) How much energy do the caterpillars get from the plants? [1]

    b) How much energy do the caterpillars pass onto the birds? [1]

    c) Calculate the efficiency of transfer from plants to caterpillar.
       Show your working. [2]

    d) The caterpillars 'lose' energy at point **A**.

       Give **two** ways in which the energy is lost from the chain. [2]

Total Marks _____ / 11

Genes

1   Put the following structures in order of size, starting with largest.

nucleus   **gene**   **cell**   **chromosome**   [1]

2   Inherited variation is caused by the genes inherited from parents.

    Which of the following characteristics are solely due to inheritance?

    A   Blood group
    B   Shape of nose
    C   Height
    D   Eye colour   [2]

3   The diagram below shows the pairs of alleles for genes that code for tongue rolling, eye colour and attached earlobes.

    Use the diagram to answer the following questions.

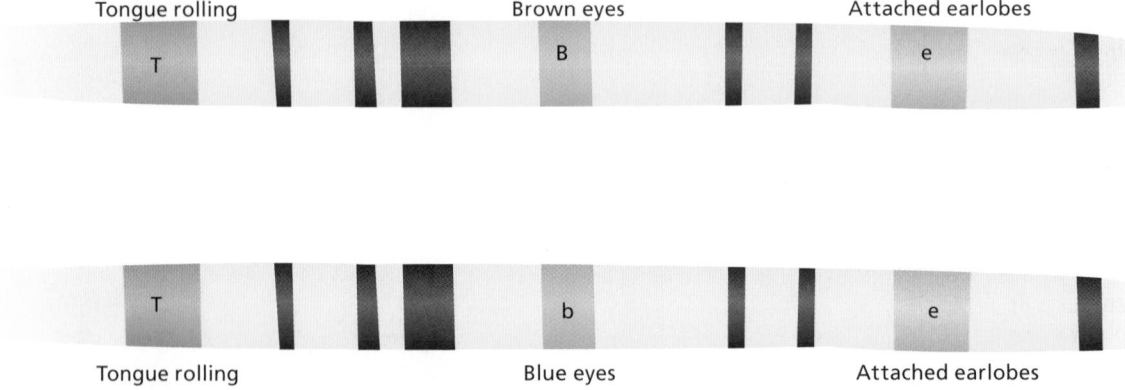

    a)   Is tongue rolling dominant or recessive?   [1]

    b)   Is the individual homozygous or heterozygous for eye colour?   [1]

    c)   What is the genotype for attached earlobes?   [1]

4   HT   Changes in gene expression can result from changes in the DNA sequence.

    Which type of DNA will be affected by these changes?   [1]

Total Marks _____ / 8

Genetics and Reproduction

1 Fill in the spaces on the diagram below to show how many chromosomes are present in each of these human cells.

Sperm **+** Egg **=** Fertilised Egg Cell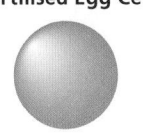

[3]

2 For each of the statements below, decide if they best describe **sexual** or **asexual** reproduction:

a) Involves two parents [1]

b) The offspring are genetically different from parents [1]

c) No gametes involved [1]

d) Provides variation [1]

e) Only one parent [1]

f) Offspring are clones of parent [1]

g) Limited number of offspring produced [1]

3 In meiosis, how many gametes are produced from one parent cell? [1]

4 The diagram below shows the chromosomes from a human body cell.

a) Does this cell come from a male or female? [1]

b) Is the cell haploid or diploid? [1]

c) A meerkat egg cell has 18 chromosomes. How many chromosomes in a meerkat body cell? [1]

5 Cystic fibrosis in an inherited disease caused by a recessive gene.
People who have one dominant and one recessive allele are known as carriers.
People who have two recessive alleles will have cystic fibrosis.

The diagram below shows a cross between two carriers of cystic fibrosis.

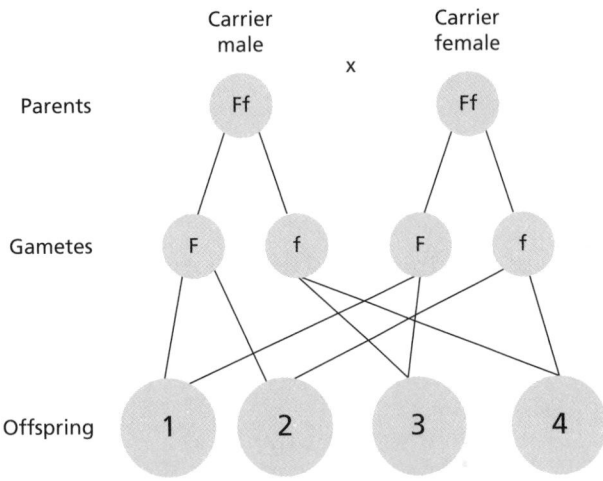

a) For each of the offspring, 1–4, write their genotype. [4]

b) What are the numbers of the offspring who will be carriers? [2]

c) Which number offspring will have the disease? [1]

Total Marks _____ / 21

Natural Selection and Evolution

1 Charles Darwin published his theory of evolution at a time when genes had yet to be discovered. His theory was based on the idea of natural selection.

a) What is meant by natural selection? [1]

b) Evolution is a slow process but can be seen quickly when bacteria develop antibiotic resistance.

Explain how antibiotic resistance develops. [3]

2 The diagram below shows a phylogenetic tree.

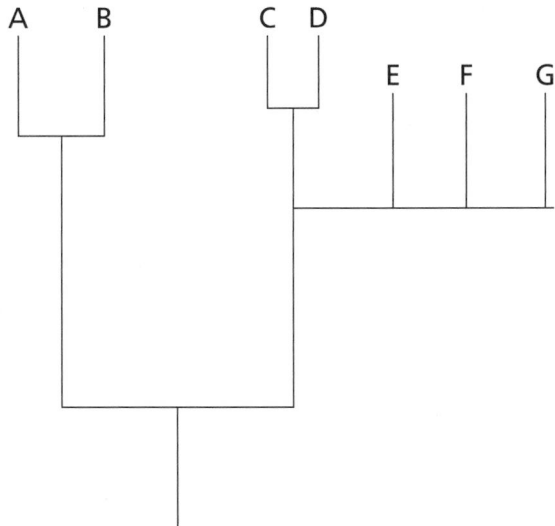

Use the diagram to decide which pair of organisms is most closely related in each question below.

a) Organisms **C** and **D** or Organisms **B** and **C**?   [1]

b) Organisms **E** and **F** or Organisms **D** and **E**?   [1]

c) Organisms **C** and **G** or Organisms **A** and **G**?   [1]

Total Marks .... / 7

Monitoring and Maintaining the Environment

You must be able to:

- Explain how to carry out field investigations into the distribution and abundance of organisms in a habitat
- Describe how human interactions affect ecosystems
- Explain the benefits and challenges of maintaining biodiversity
- HT Evaluate evidence for impact of environmental changes.

Distribution and Abundance

- Scientists studying the environment often want to investigate:
  - the distribution of an organism (where it is found)
  - the numbers of organisms in a given area or habitat.
- The following apparatus can be used for sampling:

Apparatus	What it is Used For
Pooter	Catching small insects on the ground
Pitfall traps	Catching small crawling insects
Pond net	Catching water invertebrates, small fish
Sweep net	Catching flying insects
Quadrat	Sampling the number of plant species
Line transects	Sampling the distribution of plant species

- A key can be used to identify the organisms found.

The Capture–Mark–Recapture Method

- Follow the steps below to estimate the number of animals in an area using the capture–mark–recapture method:
  1. Count the animals caught in the trap.
  2. Mark them and release then.
  3. Count the animals caught a few days later, noting how many are marked / not marked.

$$\text{population size} = \frac{\text{number in 1st sample} \times \text{number in 2nd sample}}{\text{number in 2nd sample that are marked}}$$

Using Quadrats

- Follow the steps below to estimate the number of plants in a field:
  1. Measure the area of the field.
  2. Randomly place a number of quadrats (1 square metre) in the field.
  3. Count the number of plants in each quadrat.
  4. Work out the mean number of plants per quadrat.
  5. Multiply by the number of square metres in the field.

A Quadrat

A Sweep Net

A Pitfall Trap

A Pooter

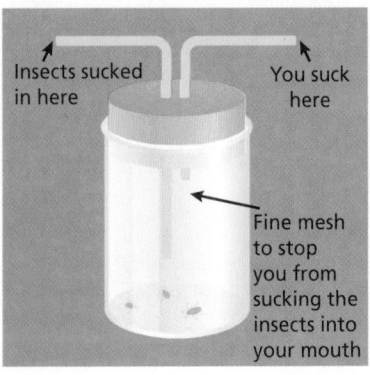

Insects sucked in here

You suck here

Fine mesh to stop you from sucking the insects into your mouth

Human Interactions and Ecosystems

- Humans need to obtain and produce resources to survive.
- Their interactions have a huge impact on ecosystems.
- Deforestation, hunting and pesticides impact negatively on ecosystems.
- Captive breeding programmes, creating nature reserves, **sustainable** fishing and passing laws to protect animals have a positive impact on ecosystems.
- **Ecotourism** aims to reduce the impact of tourism on environments by not interfering with wildlife, leaving a low carbon footprint and supporting the local community. It is an example of sustainable development.

Biodiversity

- The greater the biodiversity, the greater the stability of an ecosystem and the greater the opportunity for medical discoveries.
- Biodiversity boosts the economy, e.g. a greater variety of plants means a greater variety of crops.
- The challenges of maintaining diversity arise due to:
  - **Political issues** – conservation strategies are often politically sensitive and there may be difficulty in gaining agreements between local, national and global partners.
  - **Economic issues** – conservation is often expensive, for example, trying to monitor conservation schemes.

HT Impact of Environmental Changes

- Evidence suggests that rising levels of greenhouse gases have led to a rise in global temperatures, which melts polar ice caps and causes sea levels to rise.
- Rising temperatures also cause changes to distributions of organisms, e.g. some animal and plant species have moved further north or to higher, cooler areas and some birds are migrating earlier.

Quick Test

1. Why is biodiversity important?
2. Suggest **two** ways in which human activity impacts:
   a) negatively on biodiversity
   b) positively on biodiversity.
3. What is ecotourism?

Key Words

habitat
sustainable
ecotourism
biodiversity

Investigations

You must be able to:

- Explain how to determine the number of organisms in a given area
- Plan and explain investigations
- Select appropriate apparatus and recognise when to apply sampling techniques
- Translate data and carry out statistical analysis, identifying potential sources of error
- Recognise the importance of peer review of results.

Planning and Carrying Out Investigations

- When planning an investigation many factors must be considered and certain steps should always be followed.

At the edge of the school field are some large trees that shade part of the field for much of the day.
A group of students wanted to find out if the shade from the trees affected the number of dandelions growing in the field.

Investigation:
How is the distribution of dandelions affected by light and shade?

> The rationale for the investigation can be incorporated into the title.

Hypothesis:
There will be more dandelions growing the further you get from the trees because there will be more light.

> The hypothesis should always be based on scientific knowledge.

Method:

1. Measure a transect from the trees to the edge of the field.
2. At 5-metre intervals along the transect, place a quadrat on the ground.

> Apparatus should always be appropriate, e.g. you would not use a ruler to measure 5-metre intervals.

3. Count the number of dandelions in each quadrat.

> Scientists use sampling and look at several small areas to get a good representation of the whole area.

4. Carry out two more transects, parallel to the first one, and count the dandelions in each quadrat. This will improve the reliability of the results.

> Any data recorded should be reliable, which means readings should be repeated.

5. Work out the average number of dandelions at each distance from the trees.

Repeated transects

Trees

5m intervals

> A diagram often helps to clarify the method.

Results:

Distance from Trees (m)	0	5	10	15	20
Number of Dandelions in each Transect	8	9	7	6	5
	8	8	7	2	6
	9	6	5	6	4
Mean Number	8.3	7	6.3	4.7	5.0

Data needs to be presented in an organised way, e.g. tables are useful for presenting data clearly.

Data sometimes needs to be analysed statistically by calculating the mean, mode or median.

Line graphs are often useful for spotting anomalous results, which are often due to human errors, e.g. misreading the tape measure, or may occur randomly by chance.

Conclusion:

- The results show that the further you go from the trees, the fewer dandelions are growing, i.e. the opposite of what was predicted.

Evaluation:

- It was difficult to control variables such as the moisture content of the soil and the ground temperature, which could have affected the number of dandelions.
- To improve the experiment, a digital light meter could have been used to give some light readings for each quadrat.
- The experiment could be repeated at a different time of the year.

The evaluation should consider the method and results and what improvements could be made.

If the conclusion is different to what was predicted, the question 'why' must be asked and this may generate a new hypothesis, which can then be tested.

Key Point

Systemic / systematic errors occur when the same error is made every time. Systematic errors are only likely to be discovered if someone else tries to repeat the experiment and does not achieve the same results.

Key Point

A **peer review** is when one scientist evaluates another's experiment. This is valuable for scrutinising the design of the experiment and the validity of the data, and providing credibility.

Key Words

rationale
hypothesis
sampling
reliable
anomalous
systemic / systematic error
peer review

Quick Test

1. How do you ensure results from an investigation are reliable?
2. What is an anomalous result?
3. What are systemic / systematic errors?
4. Why is peer review important?

Feeding the Human Race

You must be able to:

- Describe biological factors affecting food security
- Describe how agriculture and farming are attempting to meet the growing demands for food
- Describe the process of genetic engineering and the benefits and risks of using gene technology in food production
- Explain how biotechnology can help in food production.

Food Security

- Factors that affect food security include:
    - the continually increasing global population, which requires more food to be produced
    - demand for a wider variety of food in wealthier populations
    - the appearance of new pests and pathogens, which can harm food supplies
    - environmental changes, such as global warming
    - the high cost of modern farming methods
    - sustainable developments, which limit food resources.

> **Key Point**
>
> Food security is all people having access to sufficient, safe, nutritious food.

Agricultural Solutions

Hydroponics	Biological Control
Hydroponics involves growing plants in nutrient solutions instead of soil. Plants can be grown at all times of the year providing the environment is controlled. Correct mineral levels can be easily provided.	Biological control is an environmentally friendly way of controlling pests. Organisms that feed on the pest (a predator species) are released into the crop, e.g. using ladybirds to reduce the number of greenfly.
Gene Technology	**Fertilisers and Pesticides**
Genetically modified (GM) plants have had genes added, which give them desirable traits, e.g. drought or pest resistance.	Fertilisers supply plants with all the nutrients they need to grow quickly and healthily. Pesticides are chemicals sprayed onto plants to kill animal and plant pests that might harm plant growth.

Selective Breeding

- **Selective breeding** is the process of finding plants or animals with the best characteristics and breeding them.
- The process is repeated many times until the desired characteristic is present in all offspring.
- Selective breeding has been used to produce:
    - disease-resistant wheat
    - dairy cattle that give high milk yields
    - wheat that grows in areas of high salt levels.

Hydroponics

Fertilisers and Pesticides

Genetic Engineering

- Genetic engineering involves altering the genome of an organism by adding a gene, or genes, from a different organism.
- It uses enzymes to 'cut and paste' genes.

Benefits of GM Foods	Risks of GM Foods
Higher crop yields	Once out in the wild it is impossible to recall genetically modified organisms
More nutritious crops	Genetically modified organisms may breed with other non-GM organisms passing on these new foreign genes into the wild population, for example, spread of herbicide-resistant genes might lead to super weeds
Crops can grow in harsh environments	We do not know the long-term effects of eating GM food; GM foods may harm the consumer, for example, causing allergic reactions
Crops resistant to pests and disease	
Better flavour food	
Food with longer shelf life	

HT The process of genetic engineering:

Steps of Genetic Engineering

1. A strand of DNA is taken from the organism that has the useful characteristic.
2. The gene for the useful characteristic is isolated and cut from the DNA using **restriction enzymes**. Some enzymes produce DNA with short, single-stranded pieces at the ends – these are called sticky ends.
3. The desired gene is 'pasted' into the DNA of the organism that requires the useful characteristic using **ligase enzymes**.

1

Desired gene

2

Desired gene isolated

HT A **plasmid vector** is a small loop of DNA often containing 'marker' genes for antibiotic resistance:

- Protein-making genes can be inserted into plasmids.
- The plasmids are mixed with bacteria.
- Only the bacteria that take up the plasmid will grow on medium containing antibiotics, due to the marker genes.
- These **host bacteria** are encouraged to multiply, producing large amounts of the desired protein.

3

Desired gene inserted into DNA of a different organism

Biotechnology and Food Production

- Microorganisms (bacteria and fungi) can be grown in **fermenters** on a large scale to produce foods such as **mycoprotein** and yoghurt.

Key Words

selective breeding
HT restriction enzymes
HT ligase enzymes
HT plasmid
HT vector
HT host bacteria
fermenter
mycoprotein

Quick Test

1. What is food security?
2. What is biological control?
3. Explain the risks associated with GM crops.

Monitoring and Maintaining Health

You must be able to:

- Describe different types of diseases
- Describe how diseases spread and how this spread may be reduced
- Describe defence responses in animals and plants to disease
- **HT** Describe how plant diseases can be detected and identified
- Explain how white blood cells and platelets are adapted to their function.

Diseases

- **Communicable** diseases are easily transmitted.
- They are caused by bacteria, viruses, fungi, protoctista or parasites.
- Sometimes diseases interact with each other, for example:
  - People with HIV (human immunodeficiency virus) are more likely to catch tuberculosis (TB) than those without HIV because of a weakened immune system.
  - Infection with some types of human papillomavirus can lead to the development of cervical cancer.

Spread of Disease

- Communicable diseases can be spread in humans in a number of ways, as shown in the table below:

Method of Spread	Examples
In the air through droplets, when people sneeze or cough	Chicken pox, tuberculosis, colds
By eating contaminated food	*Salmonella* food poisoning
By drinking contaminated water	Cholera
Contact – person to person or person to object	Athlete's foot
Animals – through bites or scratches	Malaria

- Spread of disease in humans can be reduced by good hygiene:
  - handle and prepare food safely
  - wash hands frequently
  - sneeze into a tissue then bin it
  - do not share personal items, e.g. a toothbrush
  - get vaccinated
  - do not touch wild animals.
- Communicable diseases can spread rapidly and infect millions of people globally.
- Statistics on the incidence and spread of communicable diseases are collected by Communicable Disease Centres.

Key Point

Health is more than just the absence of disease. It is defined as a state of complete physical, mental and social wellbeing.

Key Point

HIV is the virus that causes AIDS. It is possible to have the virus but not have AIDS. The virus is usually sexually transmitted and attacks the immune system making sufferers vulnerable to infection. There is no cure, but there are treatments to help manage the disease.

Key Point

Scientific quantities (i.e. statistics) allow us to predict likely trends in the number of cases of diseases and how the disease will spread nationally and globally. This is very important when planning for a country's future health needs.

Plants and Disease

- Plant diseases are caused by bacteria, viruses or fungi, and are spread by contact, insects, wind or water.
- Plants have cell walls and waxy epidermal cuticles, which form a barrier against plant pathogens.
- Plants can also produce toxic chemicals and pathogen-degrading enzymes as a response to infection.
- Spread of disease in plants can be reduced by:
  - using insecticides to kill pests which may carry disease
  - allowing space between plants
  - crop rotation
  - spraying crops with fungicide or bactericide.

HT Plant diseases can be detected:
  - in the laboratory, by analysing DNA to see if it contains DNA or antigens from the infecting organisms
  - in the field by observation and microscopy.

Human Defences to Disease

- Human's first line of defence is to stop microorganisms entering the body:
  - the skin acts as a physical barrier
  - platelets help the blood to clot and seal wounds to prevent pathogens entering
  - mucous membranes in the lungs produce mucus, which traps microorganisms
  - acid in the stomach kills microorganisms in food.

White Blood Cells

- White blood cells engulf and destroy microbes by a process called phagocytosis.
- Some white blood cells, called B lymphocytes, also produce antibodies.
- The lymphocyte recognises antigens on the surface of the invading pathogen.
- It produces antibodies that lock onto the antigen.
- The antibodies are specific for that antigen.

Antibody Production by White Blood Cells

Microorganisms (antigens) invade the body.	The white blood cell forms antibodies.	The antibodies cause the microorganisms to clump.	The white blood cell destroys the microorganisms.

Pear Rust Caused by a Fungus

Other examples of plant diseases include: virus tobacco mosaic virus (TMV) and fungal Erysiphe graminis (barley powdery mildew).

Phagocytosis

White blood cell (phagocyte) Microorganisms invade the body.

 The white blood cell surrounds and ingests the microorganisms.

 The white blood cell starts to digest the microorganisms.

 The microorganisms have been digested by the white blood cell.

Key Words

communicable
insecticide
fungicide
bactericide
platelets
phagocytosis
antibody
antigen

Quick Test

1. Name **four** groups of organism which cause disease.
2. Suggest **three** ways diseases can be spread in humans.
3. Suggest **three** ways to reduce the spread of disease in plants.

Prevention and Treatment of Disease

You must be able to:

HT Describe how monoclonal antibodies are produced and how they can be used

- Explain the role of vaccination and medicines in the prevention and treatment of disease
- Explain aseptic techniques
- Describe the process of developing new medicines.

HT Monoclonal Antibodies

- Monoclonal antibodies are clones of antibodies made in the laboratory.
- B lymphocytes, which produce large amounts of antibody, are fused with tumour cells that divide quickly.
- The resulting hybridoma cells will divide quickly and produce lots of identical antibodies – monoclonal antibodies.
- The monoclonal antibodies will bind to the specific antigen to which the B lymphocytes have been exposed.

Pregnancy Tests	Diagnosing Cancer	Treating Cancer
Monoclonal antibodies can be made that bind to the hormone found in the urine of pregnant women.	Monoclonal antibodies can be produced that bind to cancer cells. The antibodies are labelled with a radioactive substance, making cancer cells easy to see on images taken with a special camera.	Drugs that treat cancer can be attached to monoclonal antibodies. The antibodies find and bind to cancer cells, delivering the drug to the cells.

Production of Monoclonal Antibodies

Vaccinate mouse to stimulate the production of antibodies.

Collect spleen cells that form antibodies from mouse.

Tumour cells (myeloma)

Spleen and myeloma cells fuse to form hybridoma cells.

Grow hybridoma cells in tissue culture and select antibody-forming cells.

Collect monoclonal antibodies.

Vaccination

- Vaccination (or immunisation) prevents people from getting a disease.
- The vaccine contains a dead or weakened version of the disease-causing organism.
- White blood cells (B lymphocytes) recognise the antigens present in the vaccine and produce antibodies.
- Memory cells are also produced that will recognise the disease-causing organism should the body come into contact with it again.
- If this happens, they will make lots of antibodies very quickly to prevent the person catching the disease.

- If a large percentage of the population have been vaccinated, only a small percentage of the population will be at risk from catching the disease and passing it on to others.
- Vaccination is important in controlling the spread of disease. Common childhood vaccinations include:
  - MMR (mumps, measles and rubella)
  - diptheria
  - tetanus.

Antibiotics, Antivirals and Antiseptics

- **Antibiotics**, e.g. penicillin, are used to treat bacterial infections.
- They cannot be used for viral infections because viruses are found inside cells and the antibiotic would damage the cell.
- **Antivirals** are drugs that treat viral infections.
- **Antiseptics** are chemicals that kill microorganisms outside the body. They can be used on skin, on surfaces and on wounds.

Aseptic Techniques

- When bacteria are grown in the laboratory it is important to use aseptic techniques.
- This minimises the risk of bacteria contaminating the surrounding area and also the chance of unwanted bacteria contaminating the cultures you are trying to grow.
- When working with cultures of bacteria:
  - use alcohol to clean the work surfaces
  - work in a small area surrounding a Bunsen burner flame
  - sterilise all glassware and media using an autoclave.

Developing New Medicines

- New medicines must be tested for toxicity, efficacy (effectiveness) and dosage before they are released to the public.
- There are a number of stages in developing a new drug:
  1. Tested on computer models or cells grown in the laboratory.
  2. Tested on animals, e.g. mice.
  3. Tested on small numbers of healthy volunteers in clinical trials (low doses often used).
  4. Further clinical trials on people with the disease, using control groups who are given a **placebo**.

Sterilising an Inoculating Loop

Hold inoculating loop in Bunsen flame until red hot

Bunsen burner

Petri dish

Agar

Key Words

Quick Test

1. HT What is a hybridoma cell?
2. HT Give **three** uses of monoclonal antibodies.
3. How does vaccination work?
4. Distinguish between antibiotics, antivirals and antiseptics.

Non-Communicable Diseases

You must be able to:

- Recall some non-communicable diseases, suggest factors that contribute to them and evaluate data on them
- Evaluate some of the treatments for cardiovascular disease
- Discuss benefits and risks associated with using stem cells and gene technology in medicine
- Suggest why understanding the human genome is important in medicine.

Non-Communicable Diseases

- Many non-communicable diseases have contributory factors linked to lifestyle factors.
- Many of these factors interact with each other.
- For example, poor diet and lack of exercise can lead to obesity, which in turn is a risk factor for many diseases such as type 2 diabetes and cardiovascular disease.
- The arrows on the diagram below show the complex interaction of these factors.

> **Key Point**
>
> Cancer occurs when a cell mutates and begins to grow and divide uncontrollably.

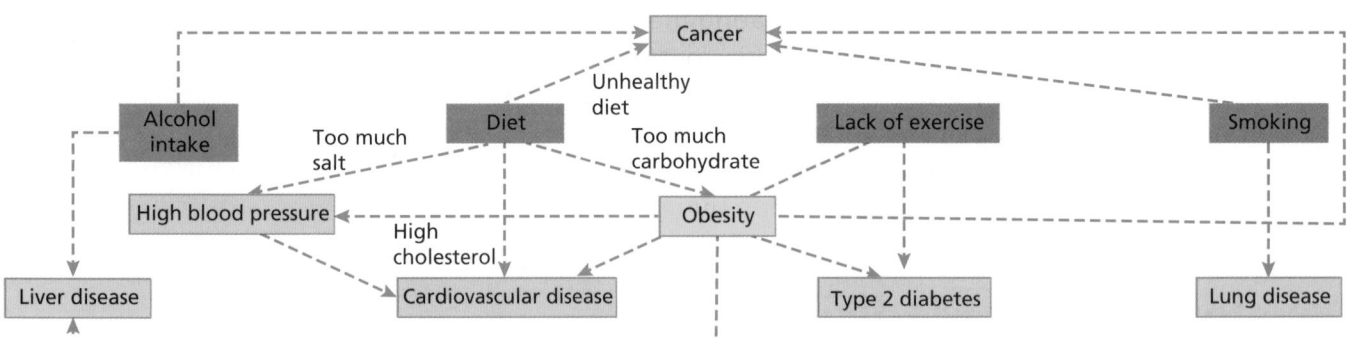

- Heart disease can be treated by:
  - **changes to lifestyle** – stopping smoking, eating healthily, exercising more
  - **medication** – there are a variety of medicines that can be taken to reduce high blood pressure, which is linked to heart disease, e.g. statins can be prescribed to lower cholesterol levels and aspirin can be taken to reduce the risk of further heart attacks
  - **surgery** – stents can be placed in narrowed arteries and heart transplants can replace damaged or diseased hearts.

> **Key Point**
>
> Cardiovascular disease is disease of the heart and / or blood vessels.

Evaluating Data

- Smoking and lung cancer in the UK:

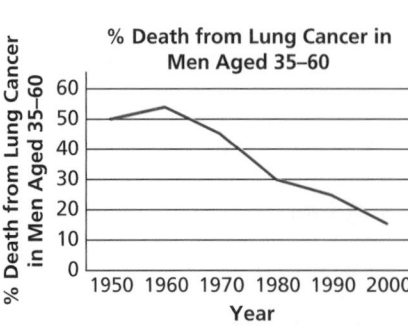

> **Key Point**
>
> You will often be asked to evaluate data to suggest the link between two variables.

- While the two graphs on smoking (on page 96) cannot prove that lung cancer is caused by smoking, they do suggest that as the percentage of men smoking decreased, so too did deaths from lung cancer.
- It is, therefore, likely that the two variables are linked.

Use of Stem Cells in Medicine

- Stem cells are cells which can differentiate to become any cell type found in the body (see page 17).
- They can be used to make new tissue and to replace tissues damaged by disease, e.g. to grow new nerve tissue to treat paralysis, or new heart valves to replace faulty ones.
- There are benefits and risks associated with using stem cells, as shown in the table below.

Benefits	Risks
Personal benefits to the person undergoing treatment	The stem cells may form tumours in the patient so may worsen the disease
Benefits to society since the process will provide knowledge that could lead to better future treatments	Stem cells may be rejected by the patient, which could lead to organ failure
Stem cells can be used to test new drugs	

- There are many ethical issues associated with using stem cells, e.g. some say that the use of stem cells sourced from human embryos is unethical and violates human rights as the embryos have 'no choice'.

Use of Gene Technology in Medicine

- Gene technology could be used in medicine to replace faulty genes, offering a cure for inherited conditions such as cystic fibrosis or diabetes.
- Replacing a faulty gene in the body has proved difficult to do.
- A virus is used to deliver the new gene and there are risks that the virus could harm the patient or deliver the gene to the wrong cell.

The Human Genome

- Genes can affect our chances of getting certain diseases.
- By studying the human genome, scientists hope to be able to predict the likelihood of a person getting a particular disease.
- Preventative action can then be taken.
- This is an example of personalised medicine.

Potential Uses for Stem Cells

Stem cells

Pancreatic islet cells

Bone marrow

Heart muscle

Neurones

Blood

> **Key Point**
>
> Some people are worried about the speed of developments in gene therapy, and are concerned that society does not fully understand the implications of these developments.

Quick Test

1. How does diet impact on cardiovascular disease?
2. What is cancer?
3. What are the **three** options for treatment of cardiovascular disease?
4. Give **one** risk of using stem cell technology in medicine.

> **Key Words**
>
> cardiovascular
> statin
> stent

Review Questions

Recycling

1 The diagram below shows a bean plant.

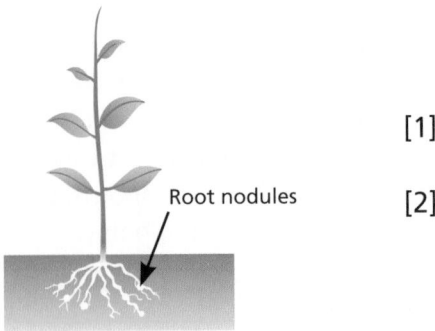

   Root nodules

  a) What type of bacteria will be present in the root nodules?   [1]

  b) Why are these bacteria important to the nitrogen cycle?   [2]

2 George has an allotment. He grows peas, beans, cabbages and carrots.
Pea plants have root nodules.
Each year George plants his cabbages and carrots where peas and beans
were grown the year before.

  a) Why does he do this?   [1]

  b) If the beans are not picked from the plant, they fall off and begin to decay.

    Give the names of **two** types of organisms that cause decay.   [2]

  c) Worms in the soil help speed up the decay process.

    Explain how they do this.   [2]

3 The diagram below shows the nitrogen cycle.

  a) What is the name of the bacteria
involved in Process **A**?   [1]

  b) What is the name of the bacteria
involved in Process **B**?   [1]

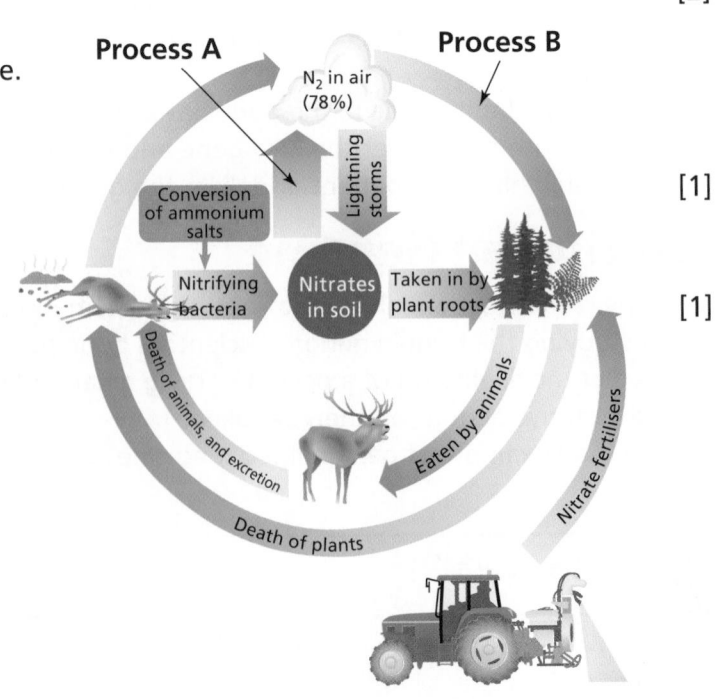

Process A   Process B

N_2 in air (78%)

Lightning storms

Conversion of ammonium salts

Nitrifying bacteria

Nitrates in soil

Taken in by plant roots

Death of animals, and excretion

Eaten by animals

Nitrate fertilisers

Death of plants

Total Marks _____ / 10

Decomposition and Interdependence

1 The red and grey squirrel live in the same habitat.

Suggest **three** things they will compete for. [3]

2 The table below gives some information about red and grey squirrels.

	Grey Squirrel	Red Squirrel
Origins	Introduced in last 150 years	Native to Britain
Diet	Omnivores – like acorns and other nuts and berries, eggs and young chicks	Mostly vegetarian but cannot digest acorns
Size	50cm; 400–550 grams in weight	40cm; 280–340 grams in weight
Litter Size	1–8 young	1–8 young
Litters per Year	2	1

Using the table above, suggest why the number of grey squirrels have increased over the past 100 years. [2]

3 In a community, the numbers of animals stay fairly constant.
This is because of limiting factors, which stop any one population from becoming too large.

Suggest **two** limiting factors. [2]

4 How will each of the following affect the rate of decay in a compost bin?

a) Keeping the bin in a warm greenhouse during the winter. [1]

b) Turning the contents of the bin regularly. [1]

c) Keeping the contents dry. [1]

Review Questions

5 The food chain below is from a rock pool on a beach.

seaweed ⟶ mussel ⟶ crab ⟶ gull

a) Name a producer in the food chain. [1]

b) Name a consumer in the food chain. [1]

c) What organism occupies the third trophic level? [1]

d) Finish the sentences about the rock pool using words from the box.
You do **not** have to use all the words.

habitat   artificial   community   natural   population   niche

A rock pool is an example of a _____ ecosystem. The plants, fish and water

invertebrates make up the _____ . The _____ of mussels in the rock

pool is likely to be larger than that of the crabs. [3]

e) While examining the above rock pool some students noticed lots of seaweed on
the beach.

i) Below is a list of factors that affect the distribution of seaweed.

Decide whether each of the five factors are **biotic** or **abiotic**.

The aspect of the beach (which direction it faces)	**Biotic / Abiotic**
The temperature	**Biotic / Abiotic**
Accessibility of the beach to humans	**Biotic / Abiotic**
The amount of fishing in the area	**Biotic / Abiotic**
The slope of the beach	**Biotic / Abiotic**

[5]

ii) There is an oil spill near to the beach.

Suggest why, in the following weeks, there is a lot more seaweed on the beach. [1]

Total Marks _____ / 22

Biomass and Energy Transfers

1 The diagram below shows the energy intake and use for a pig.

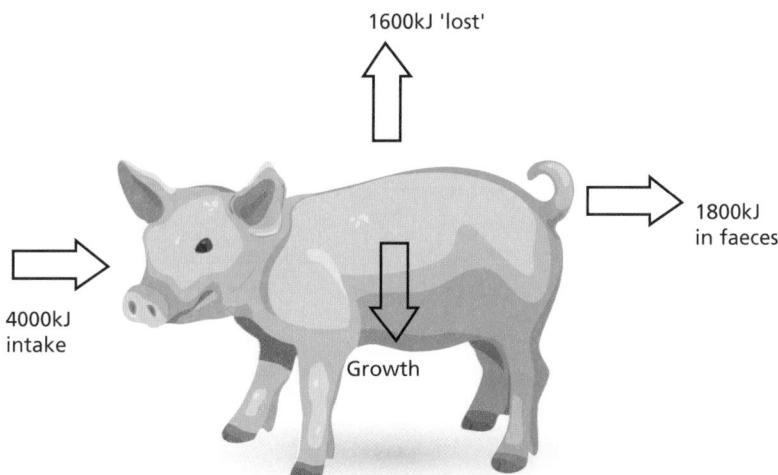

1600kJ 'lost'

1800kJ
in faeces

4000kJ
intake

Growth

a) How much energy does the pig take in? [1]

b) Where does this energy come from? [1]

c) Calculate how much energy is used for growth.
Show your working. [2]

d) Calculate the energy efficiency for the pig using the formula:

$$\text{energy efficiency} = \frac{\text{energy used for growth}}{\text{total energy intake}} \times 100$$ [2]

e) Give **two** ways in which the 1600kJ of energy is lost. [2]

2 Look at the food chain below.

plankton → krill → large fish → seal

a) Suggest a habitat where this chain would be found. [1]

b) Draw a pyramid of biomass for the chain. [2]

Total Marks .... / 11

Review Questions

Genes

1 Corey describes himself to his friend.

For each feature, state whether it is caused by **genetics**, the **environment** or a **combination** of both.

a) 1.6 metres tall   [1]

b) Blue eyes   [1]

c) Pierced eyebrow   [1]

d) Weight 90kg   [1]

e) Scar on left cheek   [1]

2 The diagrams below shows the distribution of blood groups in the United Kingdom and Asia.

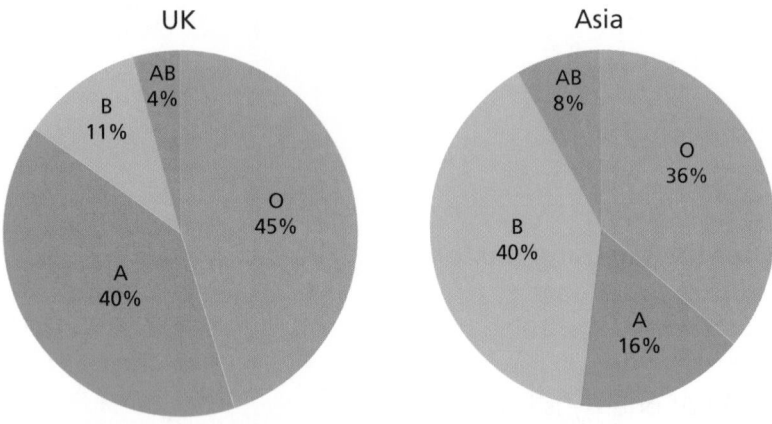

The table below contains data about the distribution of blood groups in Africa.

Group	% Population
O	50
A	25
B	21
AB	4

Draw a pie chart to show the distribution of blood groups in Africa.   [3]

3 Sickle cell anaemia is a serious inherited blood disorder. The red blood cells, which carry oxygen around the body, develop abnormally.
It is caused by a recessive gene and a person with sickle cell anaemia must have two recessive alleles.

Use the letters **A** = no sickle cell anaemia and **a** = sickle cell anaemia.

a) What would be the phenotype of someone with the following alleles?

    i) AA [1]

    ii) Aa [1]

    iii) aa [1]

b) What would be the genotype of someone who was a carrier of sickle cell anaemia? [1]

4 Lesley was studying variation within her class.
She collected information on her friends' height, weight, eye colour, shoe size and whether they had freckles.

a) Divide the list above into continuous and discontinuous variations. [5]

b) Lesley plotted a bar chart of her results for shoe size.

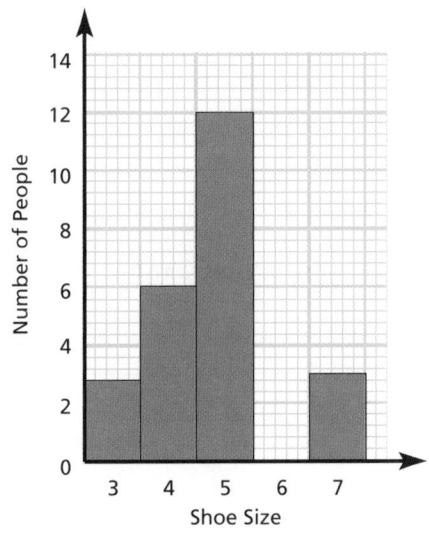

    i) Seven people in Lesley's class wear a size 6 shoe. Plot this information on the chart. [1]

    ii) Suggest how many people in Lesley's class might wear size 8 shoes. [1]

Total Marks .... / 19

Review Questions

Genetics and Reproduction

1 What is the name of the type of cell division that leads to the formation of gametes? [1]

2 In humans, brown eyes is the dominant trait and blue eyes is the recessive trait.

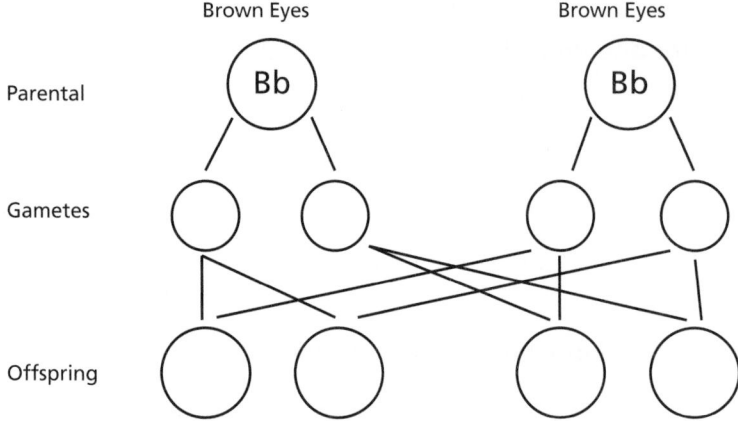

a) Complete the genetic cross above. [2]

b) Are the parents homozygous or heterozygous for eye colour? [1]

c) What is the ratio of brown eyes to blue eyes in the offspring? [1]

d) **HT** Each person's DNA base sequence differs slightly from other people's which gives rise to genetic variants.

Explain how the change in base sequence could affect protein function. [3]

e) Circle the correct option in the sentence below.

If both parents had blue eyes, there would be a **0% / 25% / 50% / 75% / 100%** chance that their offspring will have blue eyes. [1]

Total Marks .... / 9

Natural Selection and Evolution

1 In 1753, Carl Linnaeus classified the grey wolf as *Canis lupus*, the domestic dog as *Canis canis* and the coyote as *Canis latrans*.

  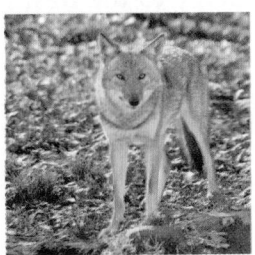

In 1993, analysis of mitochondrial DNA from all three animals showed:

- the grey wolf and domestic dog share 99.8% of their DNA

- the grey wolf and coyote share 96% of their DNA.

Following this discovery, the domestic dog was reclassified as *Canis lupus familiaris*.

a) Which of the words below describes the word '*Canis*'.
   Put a tick (✓) in the box next to the correct option. [1]

Family	
Genus	
Species	

b) Suggest why the domestic dog was reclassified. [1]

c) Apart from results of DNA sequencing, suggest **one** other reason why organisms may need to be reclassified. [1]

d) There are many species of dogs.

   What is meant by the word 'species'? [1]

2 People who have sickle cell anaemia are resistant to the tropical disease, malaria.
People with blood group O are more resistant to malaria than people with blood group A.
Malaria is more common in Africa than the United Kingdom.

Using Darwin's theory of natural selection, suggest why there is a larger percentage of people with blood group O in Africa than in the UK. [4]

3 Sometimes a mutation happens in a cell's DNA.

What is a mutation? [1]

Total Marks _____ / 9

Monitoring and Maintaining the Environment

1 Some students wanted to survey the variety of organisms in an area by a canal.

Draw a line from each survey to the best piece of apparatus for the students to use.

Survey   **Apparatus**

| The variety of water invertebrates in the canal |

| Quadrat |

| The variety of plants growing by the side of the canal |

| Pitfall trap |

| The variety of flying insects in the long grass by the side of the canal |

| Sweep net |

| The variety of invertebrates found under the hedges along the side of the canal |

| Pond net | [3]

2 Some students used the capture–mark–recapture method to estimate the number of slugs in a garden.
In their first sample they caught 12 slugs, which they marked.
In their second sample, which was collected a few days later, there were 10 slugs of which four were marked.

What is the estimated population size of slugs in the garden? Show your working.   [2]

3 Farmers **A** and **B** both grow carrots.
Farmer **A** uses insecticides on his carrots.
Farmer **B** does not.

a) How will the use of insecticides benefit Farmer **A**?   [1]

b) Both farmers sell their carrots at the local market:

Farmer **A**: fresh carrots 20p per kilogram

Farmer **B**: fresh organic carrots 25p per kilogram.

Why might some people be prepared to pay extra for Farmer **B**'s carrots?   [1]

c) The local conservation group are concerned that the number of farmland birds is decreasing.

Explain how the use of insecticides could be contributing to this decrease.   [2]

Total Marks _____ / 9

Investigations

1 Look at the diagram of a pea, before and after germination.

If provided with water and a suitable temperature, germination should take about three days.

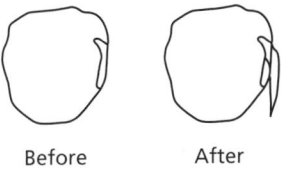

Before   After

A group of students want to find out the optimum temperature for germination of the pea.

Describe an investigation the students could do. Your description should include how to ensure the investigation is a fair test. [5]

Total Marks _____ / 5

Feeding the Human Race

1 Explain how each of the following help meet the growing demand for food:

  a) Using fertilisers [1]

  b) Hydroponics [1]

2 HT Below are the stages of genetically engineering cabbages to produce a toxin that harms insects.
The toxin is produced naturally by bacteria.

  A The gene is pasted into the DNA of a cabbage at an early stage of development.
  B The gene for toxin production is cut out of the DNA.
  C A strand of DNA is isolated from the bacteria.

  a) Put the stages in the correct order. [1]

  b) What is the name of the enzymes used in stages **A** and **B**? [2]

3 Look at the following food chain:

| Vegetables | → | Corn borer beetle | → | Chinese wasp |

Suggest how biological control could be used to improve the yield of vegetables. [2]

Practice Questions

The following statements are about selectively breeding cows that produce good quantities of meat. They are not in the correct order.

A Offspring that produce a lot of meat are chosen.
B A cow and a bull which provide good quantities of meat are chosen as the parents.
C The offspring are bred together.
D The process is repeated over many generations.
E The parents are bred with each other.

Put the statements in the correct order. [1]

5 HT Scientists want to genetically engineer bacteria to produce proteins that can be used in vaccinations.
The gene for protein production is first isolated and cut from the donor DNA.
It is then inserted into a plasmid.

   a) How is the gene for protein production cut from the donor DNA? [1]

   b) Often, a marker gene for antibiotic resistance is also inserted into the plasmid.

   What is the function of the marker gene? [1]

   c) The plasmids with the new genes are mixed with the bacteria.
   Not all bacteria will take up the plasmid.

   How do scientists isolate the bacteria that have taken up the plasmid? [2]

   d) The bacteria that have taken up the plasmid are put in a fermenter to reproduce.

   Name **three** conditions that must be controlled in the fermenter. [3]

6 HT Scientists often use plasmids in genetic engineering.

   a) What is a plasmid? [1]

   b) Why do scientists use plasmids in genetic engineering? [1]

Total Marks .... / 17

Monitoring and Maintaining Health

1 Draw a line from each disease to the method by which it is spread.

Disease	Method of Spread	
Malaria	Contact	
Cholera	By air	
Tuberculosis	By water	
Athlete's foot	Animal vector	[3]

2 The following paragraph is about tuberculosis.

Choose the correct word from each pair to complete the sentences.

Tuberculosis (TB) is a disease that affects the **lungs / liver**. People who have **HIV / cancer**

are more likely to catch TB because their **circulatory / immune** system is already weakened. [3]

3 Which of the following statements about HIV and AIDS are **true**?

A AIDS is caused by HIV.
B AIDS can be cured if diagnosed early.
C The HIV virus can be treated with antivirals to prolong life expectancy.
D The virus can be spread by droplets in the air. [2]

4 White blood cells recognise antigens on the surface of microorganisms and produce antibodies to attack them.

a) Look at the diagram. Which letter corresponds
   to **i)** the microorganism, **ii)** the antigen and **iii)** the antibody? [2]

b) What is the name of the white blood cell that produces antibodies?
   Circle the correct answer.

   phagocyte   **lymphocyte**   **blastocyte**   [1]

5 How do each of the following help to prevent the spread of plant disease?

a) Spraying plants with insecticides. [2]

b) Plants have cell walls and a waxy epidermis. [1]

c) HT Using DNA analysis. [2]

Total Marks _____ / 16

Practice Questions

Prevention and Treatment of Disease

1. HT The following statements describe the stages in the production of monoclonal antibodies which bind to the hormone HCG.
   They are in the wrong order.

A	Lymphocytes are fused with tumour cells.
B	A mouse is injected with the hormone HCG.
C	The monoclonal antibodies produced are collected.
D	Lymphocytes are collected from the mouse.
E	Hybridoma cells are grown in tissue culture.

   a) Put the stages in the correct order. [2]

   b) Suggest what these monoclonal antibodies could be used for. [1]

   c) Give **one** other use of monoclonal antibodies. [1]

2. When working with microorganisms, it is important to use aseptic techniques.

   Suggest **two** reasons why it is important to use aseptic techniques. [2]

3. Dakota goes to the doctors because she has a sore throat.
   The doctor does **not** give her antibiotics.

   Suggest why. [2]

4. Paul goes to the doctor with earache.
   The doctor prescribes antibiotics and tells Paul that he must be sure to finish the course even if he feels better.

   a) What type of organism may be responsible for Paul's earache? [1]

   b) Why did the doctor tell Paul to finish the course even if he is feeling better? [2]

5. Put the stages below, about developing new medicines, in order. [3]

A	Tests on animals
B	Tests on healthy volunteers
C	Clinical trials
D	Tests on computer models or cells grown in the laboratory

6. Explain why it is important to test new drugs before they are released to the public. [3]

7 In the early 1800s, a doctor called Semmelweiss suggested that 'something' on the hands of doctors and surgeons caused infections and could be spread from patient to patient. By insisting that doctors washed their hands, he reduced patient deaths on hospital wards from 12% to 1%.

a) What was the 'something' on the hands of doctors and surgeons? [1]

b) In modern hospitals, staff, patients and visitors are encouraged to wash their hands regularly.

   i) What type of substance is used in hand wash in hospitals? [1]

   ii) Suggest **one** precaution, other than hand washing, that surgeons take to reduce the spread of infection. [1]

> Total Marks _____ / 20

Non-Communicable Diseases

1 Beatrice has been told that her arteries are coated with fatty deposits and that her cholesterol levels are above normal.
The doctor wants to treat her with a drug to reduce her cholesterol levels.
The doctor tells her she may need an operation to make her arteries wider.

a) Suggest what drug the doctor may want to prescribe. [1]

b) What could be placed inside Beatrice's arteries to make them wider? [1]

2 Many lifestyle factors influence how likely it is that someone will suffer from certain diseases.

Explain the link between diet and heart disease. [3]

3 Ben goes to the doctor for an annual check up.
He drinks about 30 units of alcohol a week and is considerably overweight.
The doctor takes Ben's blood pressure and finds it is high.

What advice should the doctor give Ben? [4]

4 What are **two** conditions for which obesity is a risk factor? [2]

5 Which of the following statements best describes cancer? [1]

A Cells begin to grow in the wrong place.
B Cells become infected with cancer chemicals.
C Cells begin to grow and divide uncontrollably.

> Total Marks _____ / 12

Review Questions

Monitoring and Maintaining the Environment

1 Which of the sentences below best describes 'biodiversity'?
Put a tick (✓) in the box next your answer.

The variety among living organisms and the ecosystems in which they live	
The variety of habitats in an ecosystem	
A population within a community of organisms	

[1]

2 Explain how each of the following reduces biodiversity:

a) Deforestation

[1]

b) Insecticide use

[2]

3 Give **two** reasons why maintaining biodiversity is important.

[2]

4 Neonicotinoid pesticides are new nicotine-like chemicals that act on the nervous systems of insects. They do not affect the nervous system of mammals like some previous pesticides.

These pesticides are water soluble, which means they can be applied to the soil and taken up by the whole plant, which then becomes toxic to any insects that try to eat it.

Neonicotinoids are often applied as seed treatments, which means coating the seeds before planting.

Dutch scientists are concerned that their use is responsible for the decline in the numbers of swallows, starlings and thrushes over the past 10 years.

The scientists have linked decreasing numbers of birds to areas where there are high levels of neonicotinoids in the surface water on fields.

The pesticide can remain in some soil types for up to three years.

a) Suggest **one** advantage and **one** disadvantage of the pesticide being water soluble.

[2]

b) Why are neonicotinoids less harmful than some previous pesticides?

[1]

c) Scientists have data to link decreasing bird numbers with pesticide levels, but they have yet to discover how the pesticide is causing this decrease.

Suggest **two** possible ways in which the pesticide could be responsible for decreasing bird numbers.

[2]

d) The table below shows some data on bird numbers.

Average Concentration of Neonicotinoid in Surface Water in ng/ml	0	10	20	30
Number of Visiting Birds	12 000	11 988	11 650	11 600

Calculate the percentage decrease in the bird population when levels of neonicotinoids reach 30ng/ml.

Show your working and give your answer to two decimal places. [2]

Total Marks _____ / 13

Investigations

1 Some students wanted to investigate the distribution of the meadow buttercup plant in the area around a local river. They had read that the meadow buttercup prefers damp areas to dry areas.

The equipment they used is shown below.

Tape measure

Quadrat

Moisture meter

The students' hypothesis was: 'Meadow buttercups prefer damp areas to dry areas'.

a) Describe how the students could use the equipment to test their hypothesis.
In your answer you should make reference to how each piece of equipment would be used. [5]

b) Another group of students were investigating the distribution of water snails in the river.
They used a pond net to sweep through the water and counted the number of snails in the net.
They did this 10 times in total before repeating the investigation further upstream.
Their results are shown below.

	Number of Snails in the Net at Each Sweep									
Downstream	3	6	5	4	6	2	2	3	4	4
Upstream	6	1	8	7	10	8	7	6	9	9

i) Calculate the mean, mode and median number of snails in one sweep of the downstream sample. [3]

ii) Which is the anomalous result in the upstream data? [1]

iii) Suggest **two** reasons for this anomalous result. [2]

> **Total Marks** .... / 11

Feeding the Human Race

1 The graph below shows the number of hectares used globally for genetically modified (GM) crops since 1998.

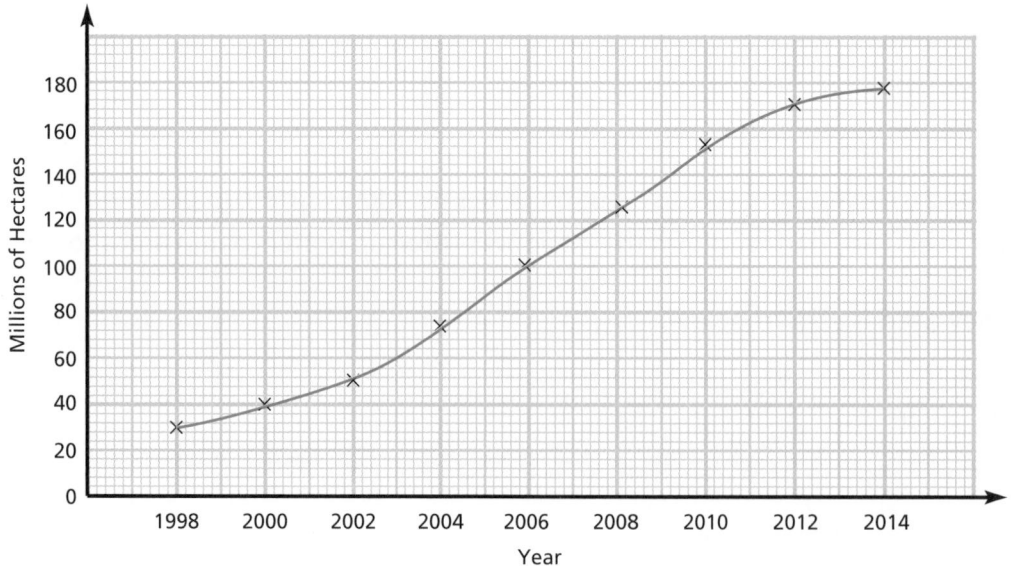

a) What are genetically modified crops? [1]

b) Between which years was there the highest increase in the use of land for GM crops? [1]

c) What percentage increase was there in use of land for GM crops between 1998 and 2014. Show your working. [2]

d) Give **two** reasons why scientists may want to genetically modify crop plants. [2]

2 Which of the following is an example of genetic engineering?
Put a tick (✓) in the box next to the true statement.

Placing a gene in barley plants to make them drought resistant	
Treating wheat with hormones to make a dwarf variety	
Taking the pollen from one type of lily and using it to pollinate a different type of lily with the hope of creating a new variety	

[1]

3 HT Genetic engineering can be used to produce rice which contains genes to combat vitamin A deficiency.
These genes originally come from maize.

Explain how enzymes would be used in the transfer of genes from the maize to the rice. [4]

Total Marks _____ / 11

Monitoring and Maintaining Health

1 Use the diseases listed below to answer the questions.

malaria   flu   athlete's foot   tuberculosis

a) Which disease is caused by a fungus? [1]

b) Which disease is caused by a virus? [1]

c) Which disease would be treated with antibiotics? [1]

2 The diagram below shows one way in which the body deals with invading microorganisms.

a) What is the name of this process? [1]

b) What type of cell is involved in this process? [1]

3 The human body has a number of mechanisms to prevent microorganisms from gaining entry.

Describe how each of the following helps to defend the body.

a) Platelets [2]

b) Mucous membranes in the respiratory system [1]

Review Questions

4 Our white blood cells produce antibodies when foreign microorganisms invade our bodies.

Use the diagram below to explain why antibodies produced in response to the TB bacterium will **not** protect us against cholera.

TB microorganism

Antibodies

Antigens

White blood cells

Cholera microorganism

[3]

Total Marks .... / 11

Prevention and Treatment of Disease

1 HT When producing monoclonal antibodies, B lymphocytes are fused with tumour cells.

a) Which of the following is a reason for using tumour cells?
Put a tick (✓) in the box next to the correct answer.

They divide and grow rapidly	
They do not have a nucleus so there is more space for antibody production	
They are easy to detect	

[1]

b) What is the name of the cell produced from the fusion? [1]

2 Tanya and Charlie are best friends.
Tanya has been immunised against measles, but Charlie has not.
They come into contact with someone who has measles.
Charlie catches measles, but Tanya does not.

a) What was in the measles vaccine that Tanya was given? [1]

b) Explain why Tanya does **not** catch measles, but Charlie does. [3]

c) How is measles spread from one person to another? [1]

d) Charlie goes to the doctor. The doctor advises plenty of rest and painkillers if necessary.

   Why does the doctor **not** prescribe antibiotics for Charlie? [2]

3 When new drugs are developed in the laboratory they are eventually tested in clinical trials.

State **two** ways that drugs are tested before clinical trials. [2]

4 In clinical trials, a control group of patients are often given a placebo.

What is the purpose of the control group? [1]

Total Marks _____ / 12

Non-Communicable Diseases

1 The table below shows how the percentage of adults with obesity in the United States changed over a 50-year period.

Year	1962	1974	1980	1994	2002	2008	2012
% Adults with Obesity	13	13	15	23	31	35	36

a) Plot a line graph of these results. [3]

b) Use the graph to predict what the percentage of people with obesity will be in 2015. [1]

c) Name **two** diseases that people with obesity are more likely to suffer from than people of normal weight. [2]

Total Marks _____ / 6

Mixed Exam-Style Questions

1 Which statement below is **not** a possible solution to the growing demand for food globally?

   A hydroponics

   B seed banks

   C selective breeding

   D use of fertilisers   [1]

2 The diagram below shows a heart.

What is the name of blood vessel **X**?

   A aorta

   B pulmonary artery

   C pulmonary vein

   D vena cava   [1]

3 Which of the bacteria below convert nitrates in the soil to nitrogen in the air?

   A putrefying

   B denitrifying

   C nitrifying

   D nitrogen-fixing   [1]

4 Some students wanted to investigate the effect of temperature on respiration of yeast.

They made a simple manometer as shown below.

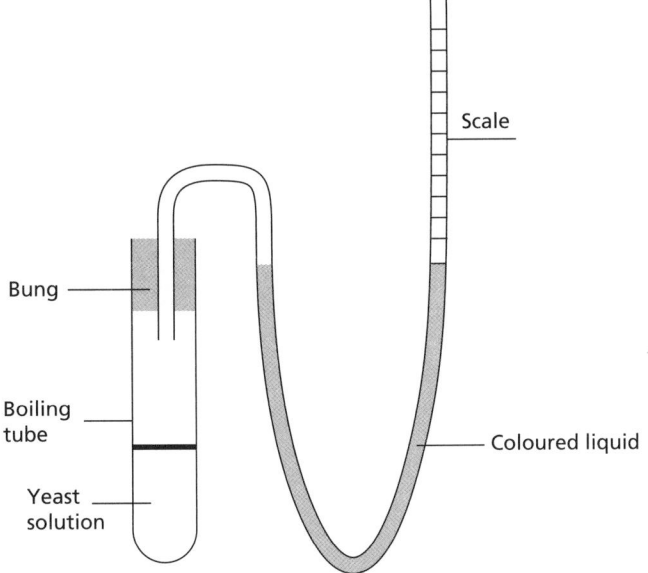

The students placed 0.5g of dried yeast, 0.05g of glucose and 10cm³ of water in the boiling tube. A thin layer of oil was poured onto the top of the water. The boiling tube was then put into a water bath at 20°C.

They left the apparatus for 30 minutes and then recorded how far the coloured liquid had moved on the scale.

They repeated the experiment at 40°C and 60°C.

a) What type of microorganism is yeast? [1]

b) The yeast is respiring anaerobically in this experiment.

What will the products be? [2]

c) Why does the coloured liquid move up the scale? [1]

d) Suggest **two** variables the students needed to keep the same for each experiment? [2]

e) What was the dependent variable in this investigation? [1]

f) The students recorded their results in a table.

A	20	40	60
Number of Divisions on Scale that Coloured Liquid Moved	12	4	0

  i) Suggest a suitable title for row **A**. [2]

  ii) What can the students conclude from these results? [1]

iii) Why was there no movement of the coloured water at 60°C? [2]

iv) How could the students improve the accuracy of their results? [1]

g) If the boiling tube at 20°C is left for several weeks, the yeast will eventually die.

Give **two** reasons why the yeast will die. [2]

5 The movement of substances from an area of high concentration to an area of low concentration describes which one of the following processes?

A active transport

B diffusion

C transpiration

D osmosis [1]

6 The diagram below shows what process?

Plant cell lengthened

Light source

A gravitropism

B translocation

C phototropism

D geotropism [1]

7 The following factors affect the distribution of organisms.

Which one is a **biotic** factor?

A light intensity

B pH of soil

C number of predators

D amount of rainfall [1]

8 The diagram below shows part of a phylogenetic tree.

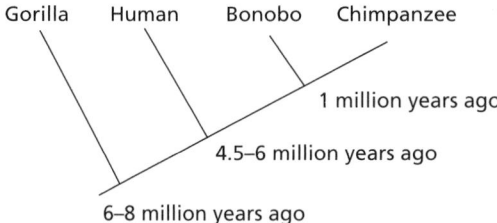

What can be deduced from the tree?

A The gorilla is more closely related to the bonobo than the human.

B The human and chimpanzee share a common ancestor from 1 million years ago.

C The gorilla and human share a common ancestor from 6–8 million years ago.

D Humans are most closely related to the chimpanzee. [1]

9 The diagram below shows the mechanism that plants use to allow gases to enter and exit the leaves and also to control transpiration.

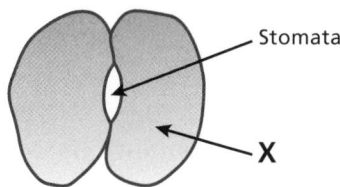

a) What is transpiration? [1]

b) What is the name of cell **X**, which opens and closes the stomata? [1]

c) Which gas will enter through the stomata when the plant is photosynthesising? [1]

10 Some students wanted to investigate if the number of stomata on the upper and lower side of leaves were similar or different.

They collected a leaf from the elephant ear plant, *Saxifrage bergenia.*

They painted the upper and lower surface of the leaf with clear nail varnish and left it to dry.

They then peeled the nail varnish from the leaf and were able to count the number of stomata in several fields of view using a microscope.

a) What is the genus of the plant the students used? [1]

b) The diagram below shows what the students could see in one field of view using a light microscope.

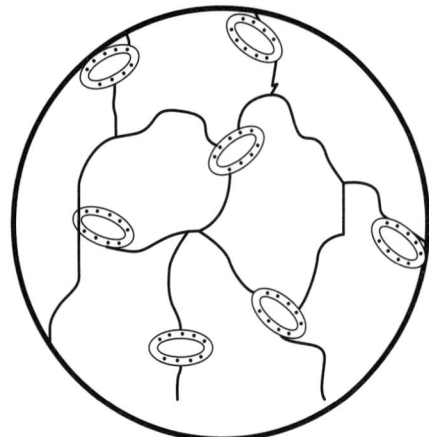

Stomata measure about 30–40μm.

What is likely to be the magnification the students used?

A × 4   **B** × 100   **C** × 10 000   [1]

c) The students recorded their results in a table.

Field of View	1	2	3	4	5
Number of stomata – upper side of leaf	2	3	2	2	1
Number of stomata – lower side of leaf	6	5	7	9	3

    i) Calculate the mean number of stomata per field of view for the upper and lower surface of the leaf.

       Show your working.   [4]

    ii) Explain why there are more stomata on the lower surface of leaves compared with the upper surface.   [5]

11 The skin is an important organ in regulating body temperature.

    a) What is normal human body temperature?   [1]

    b) How does the skin help to maintain a constant body temperature?   [6]

12   **HT** On a very hot day, the body can lose a lot of water and ions.

    Give **three** ways in which the body responds to the loss of water and ions.   [3]

13 Tall corn plants is the dominant trait to short corn plants.

A cross between two plants yielded 72 plants that were tall and 28 that were short.

What are the likely genotypes of the parent plants?

A TT and TT

B TT and Tt

C Tt and Tt

D tt and tt [1]

14 Which of the following do **not** help with decomposition?

A bacteria

B fungi

C viruses

D detritivores [1]

15 The statements below are about DNA.

Which statement is **not** true?

A DNA contains six different bases.

B DNA forms a double helix structure.

C DNA is a polymer.

D DNA is composed of nucleotides. [1]

16 Horse chestnut trees in Britain are being damaged by a moth called the horse chestnut tree miner.

Scientists have suggested a number of ways to tackle this problem.

Which of the following is unlikely to help reduce damage caused by the horse chestnut tree miner?

A releasing parasitic wasps that feed on the miner into the area

B spraying trees with insecticides

C removing and destroying infected leaves

D spraying trees with antibiotics [1]

Mixed Exam-Style Questions

17) A group of students was looking at pictures of garden compost bins and noticed they were all dark colours.

They decided to investigate if colour made a difference to the rate of decomposition.

The students took two small compost bins and filled each with 500g of decaying plant material.

In each bin they placed a net bag containing 20 cubes of apple all measuring $1cm^3$, which they weighed. They painted one of the bins black and the other white and placed them in the garden.

After two weeks they retrieved the bags of apple and reweighed them.

a) Name **two** different types of decomposer. [2]

b) How does decomposition of plant material return carbon dioxide to the atmosphere? [1]

c) The students' results are shown below:

	Bin 1	Bin 2
Mass of Apple Cubes at Start in Grams	22	21
Mass of Apple Cubes After Two Weeks in Grams	13.5	17
Change of Mass in Grams		

   i)   Complete the table to show the change in mass for each bin. [2]

   ii) What variables did the students control? [2]

   iii) In which bin was the fastest rate of decomposition? [1]

   iv) Which bin do you think was painted black.

        Give a reason for your answer. [2]

18) Scientists are concerned that more carbon dioxide is being released into the atmosphere than is being removed.

a) What process carried out by green plants removes carbon dioxide from the atmosphere? [1]

b) Why are scientists concerned about increasing levels of atmospheric carbon dioxide? [3]

19 Which one of the following is a communicable disease?

A cancer

B liver disease

C AIDS

D obesity [1]

20 Which of the following is **not** a method of detecting plant disease?

A DNA analysis of plant material

B observation of plant using naked eye

C observation of plant using a microscope

D antibody screening of plant material [1]

21 The diagram below shows the components of blood.

W

X

Y

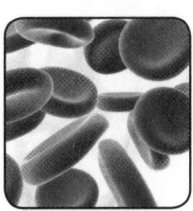
Z

What is the function of component **W**?

A produce antibodies

B trap microorganisms

C transport carbon dioxide and glucose

D help the blood to clot [1]

Mixed Exam-Style Questions

22 Which of the following is a food source that could be grown in a fermenter?

A mycoprotein

B maize

C tofu

D rice [1]

23 Colour blindness is an example of an X-linked recessive disease.

It is caused by an alteration in one gene which is on the X chromosome.

The altered gene will be expressed unless a 'normal' allele is present on a second X chromosome to 'cancel it out'.

a) Explain why males are much more likely to suffer from colour blindness than females. [2]

b) A female can be a carrier of colour blindness.

What is the chance of a female carrier and a normal male having a son who is colour blind?

A 25% B 50% C 75% D 100% [1]

c) The diagram below shows the incidence of colour blindness in a family.

Has Toby inherited his colour blindness from his mother or father? [1]

d) Toby marries Sabeena. Sabeena is not a carrier for colour blindness.

Which of the statements below is **true**?

A there is a 50% chance any daughters they have will be carriers

B none of their sons will be colour blind

C there is a 50% chance any daughters will be colour blind [1]

24 Antibiotics are important medicines, which have been used to treat bacterial infections for over 70 years.

However, over recent years, many have become less effective as new antibiotic-resistant superbugs have evolved.

a) Explain how antibiotic-resistant bacteria develop. [3]

b) Some serious illnesses such as tuberculosis are often treated with two different antibiotics simultaneously.

Explain how this regime is likely to reduce the emergence of a resistant strain. [2]

c) Why are antibiotics **not** prescribed for viral infections? [1]

d) The human body has several defence mechanisms to stop bacteria from entering our body.

Give **three** defence mechanisms and explain how each works. [6]

25 Which base always pairs with thiamine in DNA?

A guanine

B adenine

C uracil

D cytosine [1]

26 Seed banks are an important store of biodiversity.

Which statement is **not** true when considering the use of seed banks to maintain biodiversity compared with storing whole plants?

A only uses a small amount of space

B suitable for storing all types of seeds

C relatively low labour costs

D seeds remain viable for long periods [1]

27 The diagram on the right shows the parts of the nervous system.

Which letter represents the peripheral nervous system?

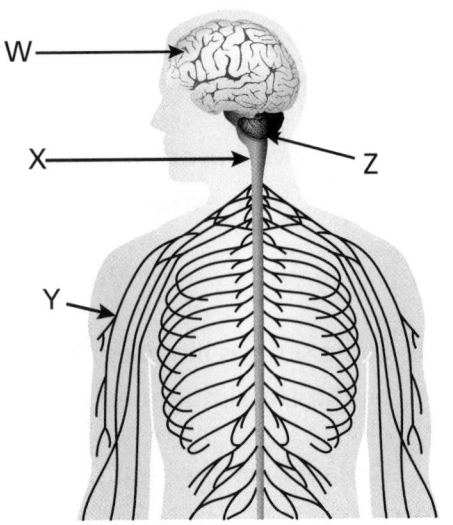

A W

B X

C Y

D Z

[1]

28 Scientists are worried about increased levels of carbon dioxide in the atmosphere.

Until 1950, the level of carbon dioxide in the atmosphere had never exceeded 300 parts per million.

The graph below shows levels of carbon dioxide over the last 10 years.

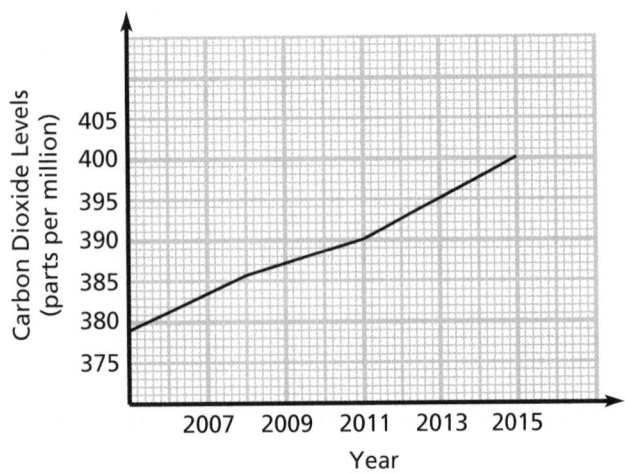

a) What was the level of carbon dioxide in 2008? [1]

b) Use the graph to predict carbon dioxide levels in 2017 if they continue to rise at their current rate. [1]

c) Explain why carbon dioxide levels have increased so much in the last 100 years. [2]

29 HT There is much evidence to suggest that increased carbon dioxide levels are the cause of global warming.

Global sea levels have risen about 17cm in the last year.

The Earth has warmed since 1880, with all 10 of the warmest years occurring in the past 12 years.

The oceans have absorbed much of this increased heat, with the top 700 metres of ocean showing warming of 0.17°C since 1969.

The Greenland and Antarctic ice sheets have decreased in mass – Greenland lost 150 to 250 cubic kilometres of ice per year between 2002 and 2006, while Antarctica lost about 152 cubic kilometres of ice between 2002 and 2005.

Use the information above to explain the impacts of global warming on the environment. [6]

30 A transgenic organism is an organism that contains genes from another organism.

By incorporating a gene for human protein production into bananas, potatoes and tomatoes, researchers have been able to successfully create edible vaccines for hepatitis B, cholera and rotavirus.

a) Which type of human cells are likely to be used as a source of the gene.

   A red blood cells

   B white blood cells

   C brain cells

   D platelets [1]

b) HT What enzymes are used to 'cut' the gene from the human cells? [1]

c) What enzymes are used to 'stick' the gene into the host cell? [1]

d) Give **two** reasons why people might be reluctant to eat these transgenic plants. [2]

Total Marks _____ / 103

ANSWERS

1. **Any three from:** nucleus [1]; cell membrane [1]; cytoplasm [1]; mitochondria [1]; ribosomes [1]
2. For rigidity / support [1]
3. They are the site of photosynthesis [1]
4. A biological catalyst [1]
5. **Any one from:** amylase [1]; carbohydrase [1]
6. They are denatured / lose their shape [1]
7. Genes [1]
8. **A** flower colour in plants [1]; **B** fur colour in rabbits [1]; **D** blood group in humans [1]
9. In the nucleus [1]
10. Double helix [1]
11. To release energy [1]
12. oxygen + glucose → [1]; carbon dioxide (+ energy) [1]
13. water + carbon dioxide $\xrightarrow[\text{chlorophyll}]{\text{light}}$ [1]; oxygen + glucose [1]
14. Starch [1]
15. Cellulose [1]; proteins [1] (Accept any other named molecule, e.g. lignin)
16. The net movement of molecules from an area of high concentration to an area of low concentration [1]

> **Net** is a really important word. Molecules will be moving in both directions so it is the overall (the **net**) direction which is important.

17. Between the alveoli [1]; and the blood [1]
18. **Any three from:** large surface area [1]; moist [1]; cells have very thin walls [1]; good supply of blood to carry oxygen away once it has diffused into blood [1]
19. cell, tissue, organ, organ system [2] (1 mark for two words in the correct position)

> The arrow means 'eaten by' and shows the flow of energy through the chain. Do **not** get it round the wrong way.

20. leaf → caterpillar → bird → fox [2] (1 mark if organisms are in the correct order; 1 mark if arrows are pointing in the correct direction)
21. Direction of flow of energy [1] (Accept 'eaten by')
22. Oxygen [1]
23. Carbon dioxide [1]
24. Carbon dioxide [1]
25. No longer exists [1]
26. A diet that contains foods from each food group [1]; in the correct proportions for that individual [1]; includes carbohydrates, fats, proteins, vitamins, minerals, fibre and water [1]

> Stating 'in the correct proportion' is important. For instance, the balance of food's in a bodybuilder's diet would be different from an elderly lady's. You need to show that you understand this.

27. Proteins [1]; fats [1]; carbohydrates [1]; minerals [1]; vitamins [1]
28. **Any three recreational drugs, such as:** alcohol [1]; nicotine [1]; cannabis [1]; heroin [1]
29. Liver [1]
30. Haemoglobin [1]
31. a) C [1]
    b) A [1]
    c) B [1]
    d) Alveoli / air sacs [1]
    e) Diffusion [1]
    f) To trap microorganisms [1]

Page 9 Quick Test
1. ×40
2. a) Mitochondria
   b) Chloroplasts
   c) Cell membrane
   d) Cytoplasm
3. **Any two from:** cell wall; vacuole; chloroplasts

Page 11 Quick Test
1. Sugar, phosphate group, base
2. a) Thymine
   b) Guanine
3. a) Nucleus
   b) Cytoplasm
4. Enzymes have an active site in which only a specific substrate can fit

Page 13 Quick Test
1. oxygen + glucose → carbon dioxide + water (+ energy)

> When writing equations, aways make sure the reactants are to the left of the arrow and the products are to the right.

2. Mitochondria
3. (Energy), alcohol and carbon dioxide
4. a) Protease
   b) Lipase
   c) Carbohydrase

Page 15 Quick Test
1. a) Water and carbon dioxide
   b) Oxygen and glucose
2. Chloroplasts
3. Enzymes are denatured

Page 17 Quick Test
1. In diffusion, substances move from a high to a low concentration (with a concentration gradient). In active transport, substances move from a low concentration to a high concentration against the concentration gradient. Active transport requires energy.
2. Glucose; oxygen (accept amino acids and carbon dioxide)
3. To replace dead and damaged cells to allow growth and repair

4. a) From human embryos
   b) From adult bone marrow

Page 19 Quick Test
1. Large surface area to volume ratio; thin membranes; a good supply of transport medium
2. They are more complex and have a smaller surface area to volume ratio
3. It achieves a higher blood pressure and greater flow of blood to the tissues

Page 21 Quick Test
1. They have a small lumen and their walls are thick and muscular with elastic fibres
2. Substances are exchanged between blood and the tissues
3. Biconcave, which increases the surface area for absorbing oxygen; contains haemoglobin, which binds to oxygen; it does not have a nucleus – therefore, more space for oxygen

Page 23 Quick Test
1. Nitrates; phosphates; potassium
2. a) Water (and minerals)
   b) Glucose
3. Wind velocity; temperature; humidity

Page 24 Cell Structures
1. Plant: all boxes ticked [1]; Animal: crosses against cell wall and chloroplasts, all other boxes ticked [1]; Bacteria: crosses against nuclear membrane and chloroplasts, all other boxes ticked [1]
2. a) i) Black / blue [1]
      ii) Pink [1]
   b) 10 × 40 = 400 [1]
3. Cell B [1]
4.

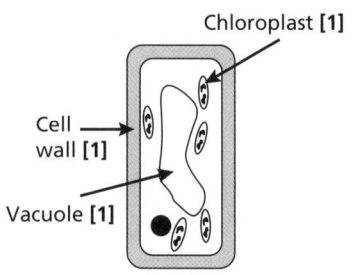

Cell membrane [1]   Cytoplasm [1]

Nucleus [1]

Animal cell [1]

Chloroplast [1]

Cell wall [1]

Vacuole [1]

Plant cell [1]

Page 25 What Happens in Cells
1. a) **From top to bottom:** T [1]; G [1]; C [1]
   b) polymer [1]; nucleotides [1]; phosphate group [1]; base [1]
   c) Double helix [1]
   d) It codes for a particular amino acid [1]
2. a)

Enzyme [1]   Active site [1]   Substrate [1]

   b) Denatured / lose its shape [1]; will not work [1]
   c) **Any one from:** pH [1]; substrate concentration [1]; enzyme concentration [1]
   d) proteins [1]; catalysts [1]

Page 26 Respiration
1.

	Aerobic	Anaerobic
Where it Occurs	mitochondria [1]	cytoplasm [1]
Energy Release	high [1]	low [1]
Breakdown of Glucose	complete [1]	incomplete [1]

2. glucose [1] + oxygen [1] → water [1] + carbon dioxide [1] + energy

Page 27 Photosynthesis
1. carbon dioxide [1] + water [1] $\xrightarrow{\text{light energy}}$ glucose [1] + oxygen [1]
2. a) Palisade cell [1]
   b) Chloroplasts [1]
   c) Chlorophyll [1]

Page 27 Supplying the Cell
1. a) **Any two from:** glucose [1]; oxygen [1]; water [1]
   b) Diffusion [1]
   c) Unicellular [1]
2. a) 6.3 − 4 = 2.3g [1]
   b) Cells of potato are more concentrated than water they were placed into [1]; so water moved into potato cells [1]; by osmosis [1]
3. net [1]; high [1]; low [1]; against [1]; energy [1]
4. **C** Osmosis is the movement of water from an area of high water potential to an area of low water potential. [1]
5. Growth [1]; repair [1]
6. a) Four correctly drawn lines [3] (2 marks for two lines; 1 mark for one)

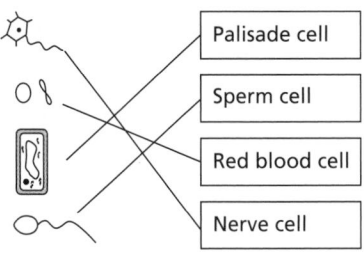

Palisade cell

Sperm cell

Red blood cell

Nerve cell

   b) **A** Animal [1]
7. Bone marrow [1]
8. Embryos are 'killed' / embryos are disposed of (Accept any other sensible answer) [1]

Page 29 The Challenges of Size
1. a) The lungs [1]
   b) Red blood cell [1]
   c) Alveolus [1]
   d) Carbon dioxide [1]
   e) Oxygen [1]

Page 30 The Heart and Blood Cells
1. a) A = pulmonary artery [1]; B = aorta [1]; C = atrium [1]; D = ventricle [1]
   b) Atrioventricular valve [1]
   c) To stop blood flowing backwards from ventricle to atria [1]
   d) The lungs [1]
2. **B** are thicker than the walls of the right ventricle. [1]
3. Capillary – smallest blood vessels [1]; and thin permeable walls [1]
   Artery – thick muscular walls [1]; and small lumen [1]
   Vein – large lumen [1]; and has valves [1]
4. **Any three from:** carbon dioxide [1]; glucose [1]; nutrients [1]; hormones [1]; antibodies [1]; water [1]; minerals [1]; vitamins [1]

Page 31 Plants, Water and Minerals
1. a) active transport [1]
   b) osmosis [1]
   c) diffusion [1]
   d) active transport [1]
2. To open / close stomata [1]; to control water loss in plants [1]
3. a) Increase [1]
   b) Increase [1]
   c) Decrease [1]

Pages 32–45 Revise Questions

Page 33 Quick Test
1. Central and peripheral
2. a) Carries impulses from sense organs to the CNS
   b) Carries impulses from the CNS to an effector
   c) Carries impulses from the sensory neurone to the motor neurone

> Always talk about nerve **impulses**, not messages.

3. a) Light
   b) Sound
4. Impulse arrives and triggers the release of neurotransmitters into the gap. Neurotransmitters cross the gap and bind to receptors on the next neurone, which triggers a new electrical impulse. The message goes from electrical to chemical and back to electrical.

> Remember, at the synapse the impulse changes from electrical to chemical then **back** to electrical.

Page 35 Quick Test
1. a) Retina
   b) Iris
   c) Optic nerve
2. In short sightedness, the image is focused in front of the retina. People cannot focus on objects that are far away. In long sightedness, the image focuses behind the retina and people cannot focus close up.
3. Using surgery, there is a danger of damaging nearby healthy tissue; drugs are difficult to deliver to the brain because they cannot get through the blood–brain barrier

Page 37 Quick Test
1. a) Testosterone
   b) Thyroxine
2. Hormonal messages give a slower response; they target a more general area; their effects are longer lasting
3. FSH encourages ovaries to produce oestrogen

Page 39 Quick Test
1. Oestrogen; progesterone
2. They are very effective; they can reduce the risk of getting some types of cancer
3. They do not protect against sexually transmitted diseases; they can have side effects
4. FSH can be given to women to stimulate the release of eggs, either for natural fertilisation for IVF
5. Social: involves people
   Economic: involves cost
   Ethical: involves morals

Page 41 Quick Test
1. a) A plant's response to light
   b) A plant's response to gravity
2. Auxin causes cell elongation on the side of the shoot in the shade. This causes the shoots to bend towards the light. It promotes growth in shoots.

> When talking about **auxins** always mention that they are found in / the response is in the **tip** of the root or shoot.

3. Auxin inhibits cell growth in the lower side of the root and the root bends towards gravity.
4. **Any three from:** weed killers; to stop or aid ripening of fruit; to stimulate root formation in root cuttings; to provide parthenocarpic fruit

Page 43 Quick Test
1. Enzymes have an optimum temperature and their action slows / stops if the temperature is above or below the optimum temperature

> Enzymes are not denatured by low temperatures, they just have a slower rate of action.

Answers

2. Sweat produced; hairs lie flat; blood vessels vasodilate
3. It causes glucose to be converted to glycogen for storage and increases the permeability of cell membranes to glucose

> Make sure you understand the difference between the terms glucose, glycogen and glucagon. Do not get them mixed up.

Page 45 Quick Test

1. High water potential describes dilute solutions; low water potential describes more concentrated solutions
2. **a)** Lysis happens when a cell is placed in a solution of higher water potential than its cell contents
   b) Crenation happens when a cell is placed in a solution of lower water potential than its cell contents
3. ADH lowers the volume of urine produced

Pages 46–53 Review Questions

Page 46 Cell Structures

1. Four correctly drawn lines **[3]** (2 marks for two lines; 1 mark for one)
   chloroplast – contains chlorophyll
   cell wall – gives support
   cell membrane – controls movement of substances in and out of the cell
   mitochondria – contains the enzymes for respiration

Page 46 What Happens in Cells

1. It becomes denatured / loses its shape **[1]**; and stops working **[1]**
2. protein **[1]**; amino acid **[1]**; speed up **[1]**; denatured **[1]**; optimum **[1]**
3. Amino acids **[1]**
4. A large molecule **[1]**; A molecule made of repeating monomers **[1]**
5. **a)** The temperature of the apple–pectinase solution **[1]**
   b) The volume of juice produced **[1]**

> The independent variable is usually the one you change / control. The dependent variable changes as the independent variable is changed.

   c) **Any two from:** size of pieces of apple **[1]**; mass of apple **[1]**; volume and strength of pectinase added **[1]**

> You will not get a mark for just saying 'apple'. You need to describe what you are changing about the apple and you also need to state what you are changing about the pectinase solution.

   d) A graph with a correctly labelled x-axis **[1]**; correctly labelled y-axis **[1]**; and all points plotted accurately **[1]**

   e) The optimum temperature for the enzyme was 35°C **[1]**
   f) Smaller intervals between temperatures **[1]**; use of two or more different fruits **[1]**
6. Transcription: nucleus **[1]**
   Translation: cytoplasm **[1]**

Page 48 Respiration

1. **a)** Lactic acid **[1]**
   b) His muscles are demanding more energy so respiration must go faster **[1]**; so his breathing rate increases to provide more oxygen for respiration **[1]**; if the demand is great he may go into anaerobic respiration **[1]**; in which case the heavy breathing will be to pay back the oxygen debt **[1]**
   c) **i)** Aerobic **[1]**
   ii) oxygen + glucose **[1]**; → carbon dioxide + water (+ energy) **[1]**
   iii) Mitochondria **[1]**
2. **a)** Fungus **[1]**
   b) Glucose **[1]**
   c) Carbon dioxide gas is being produced **[1]**

Page 48 Photosynthesis

1. **a)** Plants will photosynthesise more in warmer conditions **[1]**; therefore, grow faster **[1]**
   b) A paraffin heater will release carbon dioxide **[1]**; photosynthesis increases with increased levels of carbon dioxide **[1]**
   c) **Any one from:** increase light levels **[1]**; increase carbon dioxide levels **[1]**; use fertilisers **[1]**
   d) carbon dioxide + water **[1]**; $\xrightarrow[\text{chlorophyll}]{\text{light}}$ glucose (+ oxygen) **[1]**
   e) Carbon dioxide through the leaves **[1]**; water through the roots **[1]**
2. **a)** A = beaker **[1]**; B = funnel **[1]**
   b) Use water of different temperatures **[1]**; count the number of bubbles in a given time **[1]**
   c) **Any two from:** stopwatch **[1]**; kettle / Bunsen burner **[1]**; thermometer **[1]**

   d) There is another limiting factor / the amount of carbon dioxide / the light is a limiting factor **[1]**
3. chlorophyll **[1]**; absorbs **[1]**; water **[1]**; carbon dioxide **[1]**
4. carbon dioxide **[1]**; water **[1]**

Page 50 Supplying the Cell

1. **a)** A = sperm **[1]**; B = root hair cell **[1]**; C = white blood cell **[1]**; D = nerve cell / neurone **[1]**; E = red blood cell **[1]**
   b) To carry electrical impulses **[1]**
   c) To carry oxygen **[1]**
   d) Biconcave shape, which increases its surface area **[1]**; for diffusion of oxygen **[1]**; no nucleus **[1]**; means more room for oxygen **[1]**
   e) Bone marrow **[1]**
2. They have a large surface area **[1]**
3. **a)** Glucose **[1]**
   b) Red blood cell **[1]**
   c) A capillary **[1]**
4. Stem cells are found in meristematic tissues in plants **[1]**; Stem cells are found in the tips of shoots and roots **[1]**

Page 51 The Challenges of Size

1. **a)** Diffusion **[1]**
   b) A specialised transport system is needed to transport materials over long distances in the monkey **[1]**; *Paramecium* has larger surface area / volume ratio **[1]**; so can rely on diffusion **[1]**

> When asked about transport of materials in large and small organisms, always refer to surface area to volume ratio.

Page 52 The Heart and Blood Cells

1. **a)** A **[1]**
   b) A **[1]**
   c) B **[1]**
   d) B **[1]**
   e) A correctly drawn arrow labelled L **[1]**

Page 52 Plants, Water and Minerals

1. **a)** A = –3g **[1]**; B = –50g **[1]**; C = –20g **[1]**
   b) So water was not lost from the soil through evaporation **[1]**
   c) Plant B / plant with fan **[1]**
   d) Water lost through the leaves evaporated quickly due to the wind from the fan **[1]**; which caused more water to diffuse out of the leaves to replace it **[1]**
2. Transpiration **[1]**
3. **a)** Xylem **[1]**
   b) Water / minerals **[1]**
   c) Made of dead cells with end walls removed **[1]**
4. Active transport **[1]**

Answers

Page 54 Coordination and Control
1. a) Light [1]
   b) Ears [1]
   c) Smell [1]
   d) Tongue [1]
   e) and f) **Any two from:** touch [1]; pressure [1]; pain [1]; temperature change [1]

> The skin cannot sense temperature, it can only sense a **temperature change**.

2. electrical [1]; synapse [1]; neurotransmitters [1]; receptors [1]
3. A = Receptor [1]
   B = Relay neurone [1]
   C = Response [1]

Page 55 The Eye and the Brain
1. Four correctly drawn lines **[3]** (2 marks for two correct lines; 1 mark for one)
   Pupil – Hole that allows light to pass into eye
   Lens – Focuses the light
   Retina – Changes light into electrical signals
   Iris – Controls size of pupil
2. Optic nerve [1]
3. a) Controls automatic actions / reflex responses [1]
   b) Controls movement and balance [1]
   c) It gives it a large surface area [1]
4. a) Brain cells cannot regenerate / regrow [1]
   b) The left side [1]

Page 56 The Endocrine System
1. Four correctly drawn lines **[3]** (2 marks for two correct lines; 1 mark for one)
   Pancreas – Insulin
   Thyroid – Thyroxine
   Testes – Testosterone
   Pituitary – Anti-diuretic Hormone
2. thyroid [1]; metabolism [1]; pituitary [1]; thyroid stimulating hormone [1]; negative [1]

Page 56 Hormones and Their Uses
1. a) Less effective than the combined pill [1]
   b) Causes a thick sticky mucus which stops sperm reaching egg [1]
   c) The ovaries [1]
   d) Do not protect against STDs / can have side effects [1]

Page 57 Plant Hormones
1. a) Auxin [1]
   b) They grow towards light [1]
   c) Water usually flows in a downward direction [1]
2. The cells that respond to light in plants are in the tips of the shoots [1]
3. Three correctly drawn lines **[2]** (1 mark for one correct line)

Gibberellin – Ending seed dormancy
Auxin – Rooting powder
Ethene – Ripening fruit early

Page 58 Maintaining Internal Environments
1. a) A = blood vessels [1]; B = sweat gland [1]; C = hair [1]
   b) Blood vessels dilate, directing blood to the surface of the skin [1]; sweat gland produces sweat [1]; hair lies flat so no air is trapped [1]
   c) Enzymes work best at optimum temperature [1]; at low temperatures enzymes slow down or stop working [1]; at hot temperatures they become denatured and their active site changes shape so the lock and key no longer fits [1]

> Remember, low temperatures slow down enzyme action, high temperature denature enzymes.

2. a) Diffusion [1]
   b) Respiration [1]
3. A Glucagon is a hormone [1];
   D Glucagon is produced by the pancreas [1]

Page 59 Water and the Kidneys
1. a) **Any three from:** ions [1]; glucose [1]; water [1]; urea [1]
   b) Tubules [1]
2. a) Anti-diuretic hormone (ADH) [1]
   b) Pituitary gland [1]
   c) It increases permeability of kidney tubules [1]
3. B reduced blood pressure and high concentration of ions in plasma. [1]

Page 61 Quick Test
1. Bacteria; fungi
2. Water is needed to stay alive; the recycling of water influences climate and maintains habitats; recycling water brings fresh supplies of nutrients to habitats
3. Nitrogen-fixing; nitrifying; denitrifying; putrefying
4. Photosynthesis; dissolved in seas

Page 63 Quick Test
1. Temperature; availability of oxygen; availability of moisture
2. They become denatured and lose their shape
3. **Any two biotic factors:** food; predators; pollinators; disease; human activity, e.g. deforestation
   Any two abiotic factors: temperature; light; moisture or pH of soil; salinity of water
4. **Any three from:** food; space; water; mates

Page 65 Quick Test
1. **Any three from:** movement; respiration; keeping warm; excretion; not all of the animal is eaten
2. The amount of energy available decreases at it passes from one trophic level to the next. There is a point at which there is not enough energy to sustain more levels.
3. Joule (J)

Page 67 Quick Test
1. An organism's complete set of DNA, including all of its genes
2. A capital letter shows a dominant allele; a lower case letter shows a recessive allele
3. **Any two from:** height; weight; skin colour; intelligence (Accept any other sensible answer)
4. a) **Any one from:** height; weight (Accept any other sensible answer)
   b) **Any one from:** blood group; right or left handed; shoe size (Accept any other sensible answer)

Page 69 Quick Test
1. Haploid cells have half the number of chromosomes found in a diploid cell, as they have just one copy of each chromosome, e.g. sperm or egg cell; diploid cells have two copies of each chromosome, e.g. normal body cell.
2. Sexual reproduction involves two parents; involves the fusion of gametes; and the offspring are genetically different to their parents / asexual reproduction involves one parent; no gametes and the offspring are genetically identical to the parent
3. Eggs will always carry an X chromosome; sperm cells may carry an X or a Y chromosome; there is a 50% chance that an egg will fuse with a sperm carrying an X chromosome = XX (female); and there is a 50% chance that an egg will fuse with a sperm carrying a Y chromosome = XY (male)

Page 71 Quick Test
1. There is natural variation within any population; organisms with characteristics best suited to the environment are likely to survive, breed and pass on their successful genes to the next generation; animals with poor characteristics less well suited to the environment are less likely to survive and breed

> Don't forget 'breed and pass on genes'. It is an easy way to get two marks.

2. A bacterium mutates to become resistant to the antibiotic that is being used; the antibiotic kills all the sensitive bacteria; the resistant bacteria multiply

Answers

creating a population of antibiotic-resistant bacteria
3. Organisms that are found to have very similar DNA will share common ancestors

Pages 72–77 Review Questions

Page 72 Coordination and Control
1. a) Eyes [1]
   b) Voluntary response [1]
   c) Muscles in feet / legs [1]
2. a) Motor neurone [1]
   b) Arrow drawn pointing from left to right, i.e. ⟶ [1]
3. a) A correctly drawn bar for cats extending to 90m/s [1]
   b) Cats and humans have the fastest speeds [1]; and both are warm blooded[1]

Page 73 The Eye and the Brain
1. a) C [1]
   b) A [1]
   c) Optic nerve [1]
   d) Opens and closes the pupil [1]
   e) The light is focused on the retina [1]
2. Convex [1]

Page 74 The Endocrine System
1. a) Accept any answer between: 35–45 [1]
   b) Accept any answer between: 48–53% [1]
   c) i) Follicle–stimulating hormone [1]; and luteinising hormone (LH) [1]
      ii) The likelihood of conceiving would still be very low [1]
2. Oestrogen levels will increase from day 2 to day 14. [1]
3. a) Pituitary gland [1]
   b) Thyroxine [1]
   c) C [1]
   d) Testosterone [1]

Page 75 Hormones and Their Uses
1. progesterone [1]; oestrogen [1]; more [1]; side effects [1]

Page 75 Plant Hormones
1. growth [1]; shoots [1]; roots [1]; light [1]
2. Auxin gathers on the shaded side of the plant tip [1]; the auxin causes the cells on the shaded side to elongate (promotes growth) [1]; this causes the tip to bend towards the light [1]

> Remember, auxin is produced in the **tip** of root and shoots.

Page 76 Maintaining Internal Environments
1. a) Active transport [1]
   b) Glucose enters cells [1]; Glucose is converted to glycogen [1]

c) i) Glucose is required for respiration [1]; more energy is required in exercise therefore more respiration [1]

> Energy is **released** in respiration; it is not used or made.

   ii) The pancreas [1]; produces glucagon [1]; converts glycogen to glucose [1]; blood glucose levels are restored [1]
2. a) Glands [1]
   b) In the blood [1]

Page 77 Water and the Kidneys
1. a) Blood vessels dilate [1]; hairs lie flat [1]; sweat is produced [1]
   b) Kidney [1]
2. a) There is a gradual increase [1]; in the amount of sweat produced from 0°C to 20°C [1]; then a rapid increase above this temperature [1]
   b) As sweat evaporates it draws heat energy away from the skin [1]
   c) As the amount of sweat increases, the amount of urine produced decreases [1]
   d) Tubules [1]
   e) Increased permeability of tubules [1]; so more water is reabsorbed [1]
   f) Alcohol will cause the kidneys to produce lots of urine [1]; but the body needs to reduce urine output to make up for water lost as sweat / to prevent dehydration [1]

Pages 77–85 Practice Questions

Page 78 Recycling
1. Four correctly drawn lines [3] (2 marks for two correct lines; 1 mark for one)
   Nitrogen gas turned into nitrates by bacteria in plant roots – Nitrogen-fixing
   Animal and plant material and waste products turned into ammonium compounds – Putrefying
   Ammonium compounds turned into nitrates – Nitrifying
   Nitrates turned into nitrogen gas – Denitrifying
2. a) i) E [1]
      ii) D [1]
      iii) G [1]
      iv) A [1]
      v) F [1]
   b) Death / excretion [1]
   c) **Any one from:** combustion / burning [1]; evaporation of seas [1]

Page 79 Decomposition and Interdependence
1. B Decay happens faster when it is warm and moist. [1]
2. a) i) Stoat / fox [1]
      ii) Grass [1]
      iii) Stoat [1]

b) Rabbit [1]
c) A pyramid with the correct shape [1]; and correct labels [1]

d) Community [1]
3. Biotic: animals [1]; bacteria [1]; trees [1]; detritivores [1]
   Abiotic: rivers [1]; soil [1]; sea [1]
4. a) Hen harriers and owls [1]
   b) Prey–predator [1]
   c) Numbers will decrease [1]; because stoats are eating their food supply [1]
   d) **Any one from:** nesting space [1]; water [1]
5. a) Seaweed / phytoplankton [1]
   b) Seal / gull [1]
   c) **Any one from:** fish [1]; winkle [1]; limpet [1]; sea urchin [1]
   d) **Any one from:** seal and gull [1]; fish and winkle [1]; winkle and limpet [1]; winkle and sea urchin [1]; fish and limpet [1]; fish and sea urchin [1]; limpet and sea urchin [1]
6. **Any three from:** amount of light / shade [1]; minerals in soil [1]; water content of soil [1]; temperature of soil [1]

Page 81 Biomass and Energy Transfers
1. C The amount of living material. [1]
2. a) Lettuce [1]
   b) Thrushes [1]
   c) A pyramid with the correct shape [1]; and correct labels [1]

3. a) 80 units [1]
   b) 15 units [1]
   c) $\frac{80}{800} \times 100$ [1]; = 10% [1]
   d) **Any two from:** movement [1]; respiration [1]; keeping warm [1]; waste (excretion) [1]

Page 82 Genes
1. cell, nucleus, chromosome, gene [1] (1 mark for three in the correct place)
2. A Blood group [1]; D Eye colour [1]
3. a) Dominant [1]
   b) Heterozygous [1]
   c) ee [1]
4. Non-coding DNA [1]

Page 83 Genetics and Reproduction
1. 23 + [1]; 23 [1]; = 46 [1]
2. a) Sexual [1]
   b) Sexual [1]
   c) Asexual [1]
   d) Sexual [1]

e) Asexual [1]

f) Asexual [1]

g) Sexual [1]

3. 4 [1]

4. a) Male [1]

   b) Diploid [1]

   c) 36 [1]

5. a) 1 = FF [1]; 2 = Ff [1]; 3 = Ff [1]; 4 = ff [1]

   b) 2 and 3 [1]

   c) 4 [1]

Page 84 Natural Selection and Evolution

1. a) Organisms with an advantage will survive to breed and pass on their genes to offspring [1]

   b) A bacterium mutates to become resistant [1]; sensitive bacteria are killed by the antibiotic [1]; resistant bacteria multiply rapidly to form large population [1]

2. a) C and D [1]

   b) E and F [1]

   c) C and G [1]

Pages 86–97 Revise Questions

Page 87 Quick Test

1. Increased biodiversity offers greater opportunity for medical discoveries; it boosts the economy; it ensures sustainability (ecosystems more likely to recover after a 'natural disaster')

2. a) Any two from: hunting; overfishing; deforestation; farming single crops

   b) Any two from: creating nature reserves; reforestation; sustainable fishing

3. Tourism that aims to reduce the negative impact of tourists on the environment

Page 89 Quick Test

1. Measurements should be repeated

2. A result that does not fit the pattern of the rest of the results

3. Errors that are made every time that may be due to faulty equipment

4. It checks the design of the experiment and the validity of the data

Page 91 Quick Test

1. All people having access to sufficient, safe, nutritious food

2. Using living organisms to control number of pests / using the natural enemies to control the pest

3. The genes may get into wild flowers or crops; they may harm the consumers; we don't know the long-term effects

Page 93 Quick Test

1. Any four from: bacteria; viruses; fungi; protoctista; parasites

2. Any three from: air; water; food; contact; animals

3. Any three from: use pesticides; spread plants out; rotate crops; spray crops with fungicide or bactericide

Page 95 Quick Test

1. A cell that has resulted from the fusion of a cancer cell and a lymphocyte

2. Pregnancy testing; diagnosing cancer; treating cancer

3. White blood cells recognise the antigens on the dead or weakened pathogen that is in the vaccination. They make antibodies but also form memory cells. In a subsequent infection, memory cells produce antibodies quickly and in large numbers.

> Antibodies are produced **rapidly** and in **large numbers** in subsequent infections. These two words may gain you two marks.

4. Antibiotics act on bacteria; antivirals act on viruses; antiseptics are used on skin and surfaces to kill microorganisms

Page 97 Quick Test

1. Too much carbohydrate / fat can lead to obesity, which leads to high blood pressure and cardiovascular disease; a high fat diet can lead to increased levels of cholesterol, which coats the smooth lining of the arteries, causing them to narrow restricting blood flow and leading to heart attacks or strokes and high blood pressure; a diet high in salt can lead to high blood pressure.

> Remember, cholesterol coats **arteries** not veins.

2. Cancer is when cells grow and divide uncontrollably

3. Change in lifestyle; medication; surgery

4. Stem cells may develop into tumours / may be rejected by the patient

Pages 98–105 Review Questions

Page 98 Recycling

1. a) Nitrogen-fixing [1]

   b) They turn nitrogen in the air into nitrates [1]; which plants need for growth [1]

2. a) The soil will be rich in nitrates [1]

   b) Bacteria [1]; fungi [1]

   c) They break down matter into smaller pieces [1]; which increases the surface area [1]

3. a) Denitrifying bacteria [1]

   b) Nitrogen-fixing [1]

Page 99 Decomposition and Interdependence

1. Any three from: space [1]; shelter [1]; water [1]; food [1]

2. Grey squirrels have a more varied diet so they are less likely to be affected by shortages of food [1]; grey squirrels have two litters per year, therefore, they are outcompeting the red squirrels. [1]

3. Any two from: amount of space available [1]; amount of food / prey [1]; amount of water [1]; numbers of predators [1]

4. a) Increase rate [1]

   b) Increase rate [1]

   c) Decrease rate [1]

5. a) Seaweed [1]

   b) Mussel / crab / gull [1]

   c) Crab [1]

   d) natural [1]; community [1]; population [1]

   e) i) Biotic: accessibility of the beach to humans [1]; the amount of fishing in the area [1] Abiotic: the aspect of the beach [1]; temperature [1]; slope of beach [1]

      ii) The oil has killed the mussels, which feed on the seaweed [1]

Page 101 Biomass and Energy Transfers

1. a) 4000kJ [1]

   b) Food [1]

   c) 1800 + 1600 = 3400 (energy lost) [1]; energy used for growth = 4000 − 3400 = 600kJ [1]

   d) $\frac{600}{4000} \times 100$ [1]; = 15% [1]

   e) Any two from: movement [1]; respiration [1]; keeping warm [1]

> When answering a question on energy transfer, make sure the units used are the same for all values (don't mix Joules and kilo-joules).

2. a) Sea / marine environment [1]

   b) A pyramid of biomass with the correct shape [1]; and correct labels [1]

Seal

Large fish

Krill

Plankton

Page 102 Genes

1. a) Combination [1]

   b) Genetics [1]

   c) Environment [1]

   d) Combination [1]

   e) Environment [1]

2. A pie chart with four correctly drawn segments [3] (2 marks for two correct sections; 1 mark for one correct segment)

Group B (21%)

Group O (50%)

Group AB (4%)

Group A (25%)

Answers

3. a) i) No sickle cell anaemia **[1]**
      ii) No sickle cell anaemia but a carrier **[1]**
      iii) Sickle cell anaemia sufferer **[1]**
   b) Aa **[1]**
4. a) Continuous: height **[1]**; weight **[1]**
      Discontinuous: eye colour **[1]**; shoe size **[1]**; freckles **[1]**
   b) i) Bar correctly plotted to show 7 people **[1]**
      ii) **Accept:** 0, 1 or 2 **[1]**

Page 104 Genetics and Reproduction
1. Meiosis **[1]**
2. a) Correct gametes **[1]**; correct offspring **[1]**

Brown eyes   Brown eyes
Parents   Bb   Bb
Gametes   B   b   B   b
Offspring BB   Bb   Bb   bb

   b) Heterozygous **[1]**
   c) Three brown : one blue / 3 : 1 **[1]**

> Ratios can be expressed in a number of ways: 3:1, 75%:25%, 0.75:0.25

   d) The sequence of bases codes for amino acids **[1]**; the sequence of amino acids determines the protein made **[1]**; the protein made may not function correctly **[1]**
   e) 100% **[1]**

Page 105 Natural Selection and Evolution
1. a) Genus **[1]**
   b) New DNA evidence shows it to be very closely related to grey wolf **[1]**
   c) New fossils discovered **[1]**
   d) A group of similar animals that can breed to produce fertile offspring **[1]**
2. In Africa, people with blood group O are resistant to malaria so they survive **[1]**; reproduce **[1]**; and pass on the O blood group to their offspring **[1]**; people with other blood groups more likely to die from malaria **[1]**
3. A change in the sequence of bases in the DNA **[1]**

Pages 106–111 Practice Questions

Page 106 Monitoring and Maintaining the Environment
1. Four correctly drawn lines **[3]** (2 marks for two correct lines; 1 mark for one)
   The variety of water invertebrates in the canal – Pond net
   The variety of plants growing by the side of the canal – Quadrat
   The variety of flying insects in the long grass by the side of the canal – Sweep net
   The variety of invertebrates found under the hedges along the side of the canal – Pitfall trap
2. $\frac{12 \times 10}{4}$ **[1]**; = 30 **[1]**
3. a) Farmer A will get a higher yield because less of the crop is lost to insect damage **[1]**
   b) People feel they are healthier / safer / better for the environment **[1]**
   c) They kill insects, which are the birds' food supply **[1]**; they poison birds **[1]**; and they damage eggs or young through accumulation in food chain **[1]**

Page 107 Investigations
1. **Answer must have:**
   Suitable number / range of temperatures (minimum of 3 temperatures at between 20 and 50°C) **[1]**
   Suitable number of peas used at each temperature (minimum 5) **[1]**
   Suitable time period to leave peas (2–3 days) **[1]**
   Simple method (must include adding water) **[1]**
   At least **two** other controlled variables (amount of water / size of peas / type of peas / amount of light / same growth medium, e.g. soil or cotton wool) **[1]**

Page 107 Feeding the Human Race
1. a) Fertilisers increase crop yield **[1]**
   b) Plants can be grown at all times of the year in an easily controlled environment **[1]**
2. a) **C, B, A** **[1]**
   b) **A** = ligase enzyme **[1]**; **B** = restriction enzyme **[1]**
3. Introduce some Chinese wasps to the area **[1]**; since these will eat the corn borers **[1]**
4. B, E, A, C, D **[1]**
5. a) Using restriction enzymes **[1]**
   b) Can be used to determine which bacteria take up the plasmid **[1]**
   c) Bacteria are grown on medium containing the antibiotic that the marker is for **[1]**; only those with plasmid will be able to grow **[1]**
   d) Oxygen levels **[1]**; pH **[1]**; temperature **[1]**
6. a) Loop / ring of DNA **[1]**
   b) Plasmids can be inserted into bacteria and will replicate each time the bacteria divides **[1]**

Page 109 Monitoring and Maintaining Health
1. Four correctly drawn lines **[3]** (2 marks for two correct lines; 1 mark for one)
   Malaria – Animal vector
   Cholera – By water
   Tuberculosis – By air
   Athlete's foot – Contact
2. lungs **[1]**; HIV **[1]**; immune **[1]**

3. **A** AIDS is caused by HIV **[1]**; **C** The HIV virus can be treated with antivirals to prolong life expectancy **[1]**

> Do not confuse AIDS and HIV. HIV is the name of the virus. AIDS is the disease it causes.

4. a) A = microorganism, B = antibody, C = antigen **[2]** (1 mark for one correct)
   b) lymphocyte **[1]**
5. a) Insects can damage plants allowing microorganisms to enter **[1]**; insects can spread diseases from one plant to another **[1]**
   b) These provide a barrier to plant pathogens entering **[1]**
   c) By looking to see if there is DNA of plant pathogens **[1]**; present in the diseased plant tissue **[1]**

Page 110 Prevention and Treatment of Disease
1. a) B, D, A, E, C **[2]** (1 mark for three in correct place)
   b) Pregnancy testing **[1]**
   c) Detecting cancer / treating cancer **[1]**
2. Stop unwanted microorganisms contaminating cultures **[1]**; prevent microorganisms contaminating the surrounding area **[1]**
3. a) The sore throat is not caused by a bacterial infection / is caused by a virus **[1]**; antibiotics only kill bacteria **[1]**
4. a) Bacteria **[1]**
   b) Because there will still be microorganisms present even when he is feeling better **[1]**; without antibiotics these could start to multiply again, or even mutate into resistant strains **[1]**
5. D, A, B, C **[3]** (2 marks for two in correct places; 1 mark for one)
6. To test for efficacy / efficiency **[1]**; toxicity / safety **[1]**; dosage **[1]**
7. a) Bacteria / microorganisms **[1]**
   b) i) Antiseptic **[1]**
      ii) **Any one from:** gloves **[1]**; masks **[1]**; gowns **[1]**; all equipment sterilised **[1]**

Page 111 Non-Communicable Diseases
1. a) Statins **[1]**
   b) A stent **[1]**
2. High fat diet can lead to high cholesterol **[1]**; which narrows arteries **[1]**; causing high blood pressure, which puts a strain on heart **[1] OR** high salt intake **[1]**; causes high blood pressure **[1]**; which puts a strain on heart **[1] OR** eating more kJ energy / calories than used **[1]** leads to obesity **[1]**; which causes cardiovascular disease **[1]**
3. **Any four from:** drink less alcohol **[1]**; eat less **[1]**; lower salt intake **[1]**; switch to low fat products **[1]**; exercise more **[1]**

4. Any two from: Type 2 diabetes [1]; joint problems [1]; heart disease [1]; high blood pressure [1]; high cholesterol [1]

5. C Cells begin to grow and divide uncontrollably. [1]

Pages 112–117 Review Questions

Page 112 Monitoring and Maintaining the Environment

1. The variety among living organisms and the ecosystems in which they live [1]
2. a) Destroys habitats [1]
   b) Kill insects [1]; disrupts food chains [1]
3. **Any two from:** may lead to new medicines [1]; cures for diseases [1]; better economy [1]; ensures sustainability [1]
4. a) Advantage: can be applied to soil and will be taken in by plants [1] Disadvantage: can be washed away into water courses, rivers, etc. and can get into animals that drink the water [1]
   b) They do not affect the nervous system of mammals [1]
   c) The birds are consuming the pesticide when they drink water and this is harming them [1]; the birds are starving because the pesticide is killing their food source [1]
   d) Decrease = 12000 − 11600 = 400 [1]; % decrease = $\frac{400}{12000} \times 100 = 3.33\%$ [1]

Page 113 Investigations

1. a) Use the tape measure to mark a transect line from the river outwards across the field [1]; at suitable intervals, place a quadrat [1]; count the number of meadow buttercups in the quadrant [1]; measure the moisture content of the soil using the moisture meter [1]; repeat the transect in different areas / repeat and calculate and average [1]
   b) i) Mean = 39 ÷ 10 = 3.9 [1]; mode = 4 [1]; median = 4 [1]
      ii) 1 [1]
      iii) **Any two from:** chance [1]; error made in counting [1]; net swept at different level [1]; net swept in different direction / angle [1]

Page 114 Feeding the Human Race

1. a) Plants which have had their DNA changed, usually by addition of useful gene from another organism [1]
   b) 2002 and 2010 [1]
   c) $\frac{180}{30} \times 100$ [1]; = 600% [1]
   d) **Any two from:** insecticide resistance [1]; drought resistance [1]; able to grow in salty water [1]; increased nutritional content; increased shelf life [1]
2. Placing a gene in barley plants to make them drought resistant [1]
3. Restriction enzyme [1]; to cut the gene from the maize plant DNA [1]; Ligase enzyme [1]; to paste the gene into rice plant DNA (or accept plasmid) [1]

Page 115 Monitoring and Maintaining Health

1. a) Athlete's foot [1]
   b) Flu [1]
   c) Tuberculosis [1]
2. a) Phagocytosis [1]

> Remember, the word **phagocytosis** means to devour the cell.

   b) A phagocyte [1]
3. a) Form a clot [1]; which seals the wound [1]
   b) Trap microorganisms and dirt [1]
4. The antibodies produced against the tuberculosis (TB) bacterium are designed to recognise and lock onto the antigens on its surface (or accept: specific to TB bacteria) [1]; the antigens on the cholera virus are different [1]; and the TB antibodies will not recognise them or fit onto them [1]

Page 116 Prevention and Treatment of Disease

1. a) They divide and grow rapidly [1]
   b) Hybridoma [1]
2. a) Dead / weakened measles virus [1]
   b) Tanya already had antibodies against the measles virus [1]; she also has memory cells [1]; which can quickly produce large numbers of antibodies [1]
   c) In the air / moisture droplets [1]
   d) Measles in caused by a virus [1]; antibiotics cannot be used for viral infections / can only be used for bacterial infections [1]
3. **Any two from:** tested on cells [1]; animals [1]; computer models [1]; healthy volunteers [1]
4. To compare the results of people taking the drug to those who have not taken the drug [1]

Page 117 Non-Communicable Diseases

1. a) Correctly labelled axes [1]; correctly plotted points [1]; joined by a smooth curve [1]

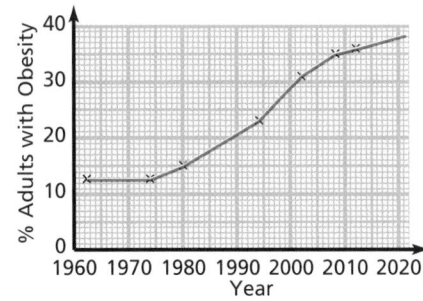

   b) 37% [1]
   c) **Any two from:** heart disease [1]; type 2 diabetes [1]; high blood pressure [1]; liver disease [1]

Pages 118–129 Mixed Exam-Style Questions

1. **B** seed banks [1]
2. **A** aorta [1]
3. **B** denitrifying [1]
4. a) A fungus [1]
   b) Ethanol [1]; carbon dioxide [1]
   c) Pressure caused by carbon dioxide gas [1]
   d) **Any two from:** amount of yeast [1]; amount of glucose [1]; volume of water [1]; incubation time [1]
   e) Units that liquid moved up the scale [1]
   f) i) Temperature [1]; °C [1]
      ii) The yeast respires at a faster rate at a temperature of 20°C [1]
      iii) The enzymes [1]; in the yeast had been denatured / were destroyed by the high temperature [1]
      iv) Use a smaller range of temperatures / smaller divisions on the scale [1]
   g) The yeast will run out of glucose [1]; the yeast is killed by increasing concentrations of ethanol [1]
5. **B** diffusion [1]
6. **C** phototropism [1]
7. **C** number of predators [1]
8. **C** The gorilla and human share a common ancestor from 6–8 million years ago. [1]
9. a) Movement of water through a plant and its evaporation from the leaves [1]
   b) Guard cell [1]
   c) Carbon dioxide [1]
10. a) *Saxifrage* [1]
    b) B × 100 [1]
    c) i) Upper: $\frac{10}{5}$ [1]; = 2 [1]; lower: $\frac{30}{5}$ [1]; = 6 [1]
       ii) On a hot day plants will open their stomata [1]; to allow exchange of gases [1]; for photosynthesis [1]; plants will lose less water through evaporation [1]; if the stomata are not in direct sunlight / are shaded [1]
11. a) 37°C [1]
    b) **Any six of following points:** temperature rise in the blood is detected by the hypothalamus [1]; blood vessels in the skin dilate [1]; increasing blood flow to the skin [1]; sweat glands produce sweat [1]; evaporation of sweat uses heat energy from the body [1]; hairs lie flat [1]; results in a return to normal temperature, which is detected by the hypothalamus [1]; temperature drop of the blood is detected by the hypothalamus [1]; blood vessels in the skin constrict, decreasing blood flow to the skin [1]; hairs stand up [1]; trap air, which is an insulator [1]; shivering [1]; which generates heat [1]

Answers

12. Reduces urine output [1]; kidney tubules reabsorb more water and ions [1]; thirst mechanism activated [1]
13. **C** Tt and Tt [1]
14. **C** viruses [1]
15. **A** DNA contains six different bases [1]
16. **D** spraying trees with antibiotics [1]
17. a) Bacteria [1]; fungi [1]
    b) The microorganisms that decompose the material respire [1]
    c) i) Bin 1: 8.5g [1]; Bin 2: 4g [1]
       ii) **Any two from:** Mass of plant material [1]; number [1]; size [1]; mass of apple cubes [1]; time left [1]
       iii) Bin 1 [1]
       iv) Bin 1 because black absorbs heat [1]; the rate of decomposition increases with temperature [1]
18. a) Photosynthesis [1]
    b) It is a greenhouse gas [1]; and traps heat energy reflected from the earth [1]; causing global warming [1]
19. **C** AIDS [1]
20. **D** antibody screening of plant material [1]
21. **D** help the blood to clot [1]
22. **A** mycoprotein [1]
23. a) Males only have one X chromosome [1]; so if the allele for colour blindness is present, there is no

chance of a second allele to cancel it out [1]
    b) **B** 50% [1]
    c) Mother [1]
    d) **B** none of their sons will be colour blind [1]
24. a) A mutation occurs that makes the bacterium resistant [1]; the sensitive bacteria are killed by the antibiotic [1]; the resistant bacteria survive and multiply to form a resistant population [1]
    b) If a bacterium mutates to develop resistance to one antibiotic [1]; it is still likely to be killed by the second antibiotic [1]
    c) Antibiotics are not effective against viruses / only kill bacteria [1]
    d) **Any three defences, plus a correct explanation for a total of 6 marks:** skin [1]; physical barrier [1] OR platelets [1]; form clot to seal wounds [1] OR mucous membranes [1]; trap microorganisms [1] OR acid in stomach [1]; kills microorganisms [1] OR tears / sweat [1]; contain antimicrobial substances [1]
25. **B** adenine [1]
26. **B** suitable for storing all types of seeds [1]

27. **C** Y [1]
28. a) **Accept:** 385.5 **OR** 386ppm [1]
    b) **Accept any value between:** 404–406ppm [1]
    c) Increase in the burning of fossil fuels [1]; deforestation [1]
29. Sea levels will rise / coastal areas flooded [1]; resulting in loss of habitat / disruption to food chain [1]; rising temperatures result in organisms not able to survive where previously they had thrived [1]; ice sheets melting causes loss of habitat for animals that live there [1]; all of which causes loss of biodiversity [1]; and the migration patterns of birds are affected [1]
30. a) **B** white blood cells [1]
    b) Restriction enzymes [1]
    c) Ligase enzymes [1]
    d) Worried about safety for consumption / long-term effects not known [1]; dislike the idea of eating something that contains human genes [1]

> If asked for concerns about genetically engineered foods, your answer must include concerns about safety when **eaten / consumed**.

Glossary and Index

Potometer   apparatus used for measuring transpiration rate in plants   23

Precise   referring to data that is accurate and reliable   18

Predation   the preying of one animal on others   63

Progesterone   a hormone produced by the ovaries   37

Prokaryote   simple cell with no nuclear membrane   9

Pupil   the hole in the middle of the eye, which lets light in   34

R

Rationale   reason for doing something   88

Receptor   parts of sense organs that receive stimuli from the environment   32

Receptor molecules   protein molecules that receive chemical signals from outside the cell   9

Recessive   a characteristic only expressed if both alleles for that characteristic are present   66

Reliable   refers to results that are repeatable and reproducible   88

Repeatable   refers to results that will be shown again if the same experiment is performed again   18

Reproducible   refers to results that will be found again if the same experiment is performed by another person   18

Resolution   the ability to distinguish two objects when separated by a small distance   8

HT **Restriction enzyme**   enzyme used in genetic engineering to 'cut' genes from DNA   91

Retina   the part of the eye that changes the light into electrical impulses   34

S

Sampling   surveying a number of small portions, which are representative of the total portion, to allow an estimate to be made for the whole portion   88

Selective breeding   breeding two adult organisms to get offspring with certain desired characteristics   90

Selective reabsorption   absorbing only certain molecules   44

Stain   dye used to colour cells and cell structures   8

Statin   drug given to reduce cholesterol levels in the body   96

Stent   a small mesh tube used to inflate blocked arteries   96

Stimulus / stimuli (pl.)   something that can elicit (give rise to) a response   32

Stomata   pores in the underside of a leaf, which are opened and closed by guard cells, that allow gases in and out   23

Substrate   the molecule upon which an enzyme acts (the key)   11

Suspensory ligaments   hold the lens in place and can alter the shape of the lens   34

Sustainable   refers to methods with minimal impact on the environment   87

Systemic / systematic error   an error that is made repeatedly, e.g. using a balance that has not been calibrated correctly   89

Synapse   the gap between two nerve cells   32

T

Tubule   part of the nephron; where selective reabsorption takes places   44

Translocation   movement of glucose in plants   22

U

Unicellular   an organism that has only one cell   18

Urea   waste product of amino acid breakdown which is excreted in urine   18

V

Variant altered gene that forms when DNA is copied   67

Vasoconstriction   blood vessels become narrow so flow of blood is constricted   42

Vasodilation   blood vessels become wider allowing more blood to flow   42

HT **Vector**   DNA molecules used to transfer genes from one organism to another   91

Ventricles   the bottom chambers of the heart   20

Notes

Notes

Collins

OCR GCSE Revision

Biology

Biology

OCR
Gateway
GCSE

Workbook

Fran Walsh

Revision Tips

Rethink Revision

Have you ever taken part in a quiz and thought *'I know this!'* but, despite frantically racking your brain, you just couldn't come up with the answer?

It's very frustrating when this happens but, in a fun situation, it doesn't really matter. However, in your GCSE exams, it will be essential that you can recall the relevant information quickly when you need to.

Most students think that revision is about making sure you **know** stuff. Of course, this is important, but it is also about becoming confident that you can **retain** that *stuff* over time and **recall** it quickly when needed.

Revision That Really Works

Experts have discovered that there are two techniques that help with all of these things and consistently produce better results in exams compared to other revision techniques.

Applying these techniques to your GCSE revision will ensure you get better results in your exams and will have all the relevant knowledge at your fingertips when you start studying for further qualifications, like AS and A Levels, or begin work.

It really isn't rocket science either – you simply need to:

- **test yourself** on each topic as many times as possible
- **leave a gap** between the test sessions.

Three Essential Revision Tips

1. **Use Your Time Wisely**

   - Allow yourself plenty of time.
   - Try to start revising at least six months before your exams – it's more effective and less stressful.
   - Your revision time is precious so use it wisely – using the techniques described on this page will ensure you revise effectively and efficiently and get the best results.
   - Don't waste time re-reading the same information over and over again – it's time-consuming and not effective!

2. **Make a Plan**

   - Identify all the topics you need to revise (this All-in-One Revision & Practice book will help you).
   - Plan at least five sessions for each topic.
   - One hour should be ample time to test yourself on the key ideas for a topic.
   - Spread out the practice sessions for each topic – the optimum time to leave between each session is about one month but, if this isn't possible, just make the gaps as big as realistically possible.

3. **Test Yourself**

   - Methods for testing yourself include: quizzes, practice questions, flashcards, past papers, explaining a topic to someone else, etc.
   - This All-in-One Revision & Practice book provides seven practice opportunities per topic.
   - Don't worry if you get an answer wrong – provided you check what the correct answer is, you are more likely to get the same or similar questions right in future!

Visit our website to download your free flashcards, for more information about the benefits of these techniques, and for further guidance on how to plan ahead and make them work for you.

www.collins.co.uk/collinsGCSErevision

Contents

Cell Structures

1 **a)** Draw a line from each cellular structure to its function.

Structure	Function
Nucleus	Contains chlorophyll
Cell membrane	Contains receptor molecules
Chloroplast	Contains enzymes for respiration
Mitochondria	Contains genetic material

[3]

b) Which of the structures above is only found in plant cells?

.... [1]

2 Which of the following are features of an electron microscope? Tick (✓) **two** boxes.

Higher resolution than light microscope	
Does not require specimens to be stained	
Uses more powerful lenses than a light microscope	
Uses magnets to focus an electron beam	

[2]

3 Jade wants to look at some blood using a light microscope.
She pricks her finger and places a drop of blood on a glass slide.

a) Once the blood has dried, what can Jade do to make the cells easier to see under
the microscope?

....

b) The diagram shows what Jade can see under the microscope.

   i) What type of cell is cell **X**?

   .... [1]

   ii) What type of cell is cell **Y**?

   .... [1]

c) Jade is using a microscope with a ×4 magnification eyepiece and a ×100 magnification
objective lens.

What is the total magnification she is using?

.... [1]

Total Marks .... / 9

What Happens in Cells

1 Which of the following statements about DNA are correct? Tick (✓) **three** boxes.

DNA is a monomer	
DNA is made of two strands arranged in a double helix	
DNA is made of nucleotides	
DNA contains six different bases	
Triplet codes in DNA code for amino acids	
Most of the cell's DNA is found in the mitochondria	

[3]

2 **a)** Protease enzyme digests proteins. What does carbohydrase enzyme digest?

_____ [1]

b) An enzyme reaction can be summarised as: enzyme + substrate ⟶ products (+ enzyme)

Complete the equation to show the reaction for lipase enzyme.

lipase + _____ ⟶ _____ + _____ (+ lipase) [3]

c) Enzymes are denatured by high temperatures. Suggest **one** other factor that may denature enzymes.

_____ [1]

3 The diagram below shows a section of DNA. The sequence of bases on one side is shown.

a) Complete the diagram to show the missing bases. [1]

b) How many bases code for one amino acid? _____ [1]

c) When proteins are made, the DNA 'unzips' so that mRNA can make a copy of the one strand.

i) What is this process called?

_____ [1]

ii) Where in the cell does this process happen?

_____ [1]

4 The enzyme amylase breaks down starch. It is present in saliva.

Explain why amylase stops working when it reaches the stomach.

_____ [2]

Total Marks _____ / 14

Respiration

1. The table below shows the percentage of a person's blood that is delivered to different areas of the body during exercise and at rest.

Body Parts	Percentage of Blood Delivered to Each Part	
	At Rest	During Exercise
Muscles	15	65
Brain	17	5
Liver	30	8
Other	38	22

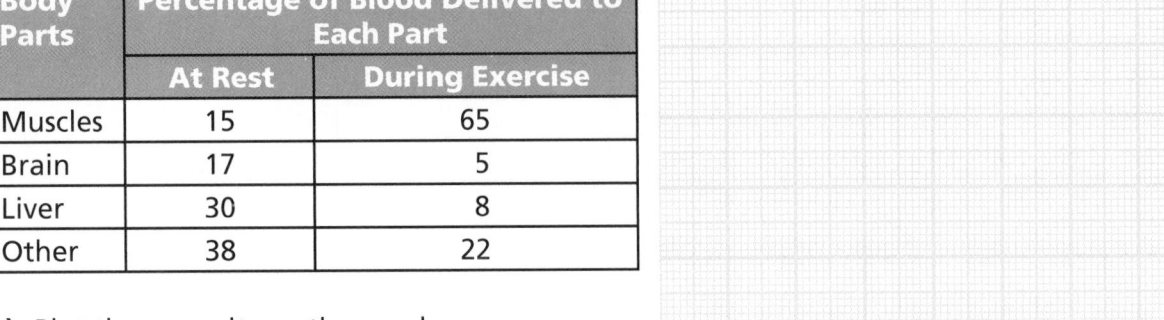

a) Plot these results on the graph paper. [5]

b) Suggest why there is more blood flowing to the muscles during exercise than at rest.

_____

_____

_____ [3]

2. The diagram shows a yeast cell.

a) To what group of microorganisms does yeast belong?

_____ [1]

b) Which **two** structures are present in both yeast and plants cells, but not animal cells?

_____

_____ [2]

c) Yeast can respire in the absence of oxygen. Write the word equation for this reaction.

_____ [3]

3. Most living things use oxygen when they respire. This is known as aerobic respiration.

a) Write the word equation for aerobic respiration.

_____ [2]

b) How are the reactants in this equation delivered to body cells?

_____ [1]

Total Marks _____ / 17

Photosynthesis

1 The following questions are about plants and food:

a) What is the name of the process plants use to make food?

_____ [1]

b) What is the name of the food molecule made by plants?

_____ [1]

c) What is this food molecule used for?

_____

_____ [2]

d) Explain why the concentration of carbon dioxide in a greenhouse may be higher at night than during the day.

_____

_____

_____ [2]

2 a) Complete the word equation for photosynthesis.

$$\text{carbon dioxide} + \underline{\hspace{3cm}} \xrightarrow[\text{chlorophyll}]{\text{light energy}} \text{glucose} + \underline{\hspace{2cm}}$$

[2]

b) Complete the symbol equation for photosynthesis.

$$6CO_2 + \underline{\hspace{3cm}} \xrightarrow[\text{chlorophyll}]{\text{light energy}} C_6H_{12}O_6 + \underline{\hspace{2cm}}$$

[2]

c) The chlorophyll needed for photosynthesis is found inside which subcellular structures?

_____

d) Photosynthesis is an endothermic reaction. What does this mean?

_____ [1]

e) Apart from the amount of light, state **two** other factors that limit photosynthesis.

_____ [2]

Total Marks _____ / 13

Supplying the Cell

1 The diagram below shows the stages in the cell cycle.

A   B   C   D   E

a) Put the stages in the correct order. The first one has been done for you.

B .... [1]

b) What is the name of the type of cell division shown in the diagram?

.... [1]

c) Apart from growth, state **one** other reason for this type of cell division.

.... [1]

2 The boxes below represent the concentrations of salts inside and outside a cell.

| Low salt concentration | | High salt concentration |

Draw three arrows on the diagram and label them to show the direction of movement for:

a) diffusion   b) active transport   c) movement of water by osmosis.   [3]

3 A stem cell is a cell that can differentiate into many different types of cell.

a) Name **two** places from where human stem cells can be obtained.

.... [2]

b) The diagram shows two cells that have differentiated to become specialised cells.

Name each cell and describe how it is adapted to its function.

X   Y

X ....

....

Y ....

.... [6]

Total Marks .... / 14

The Challenges of Size

1 The diagram shows two cells from different parts of a plant.

a) What is the name of cell **Y**?

_____ [1]

b) In which part of a plant would you find cell **Z**?

_____ [1]

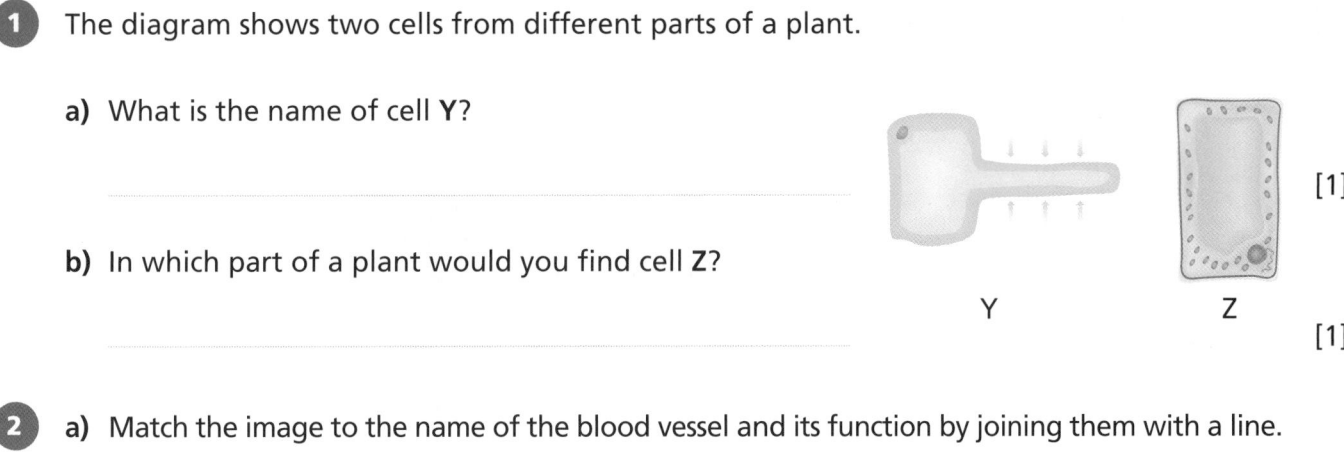

Y   Z

2 a) Match the image to the name of the blood vessel and its function by joining them with a line.

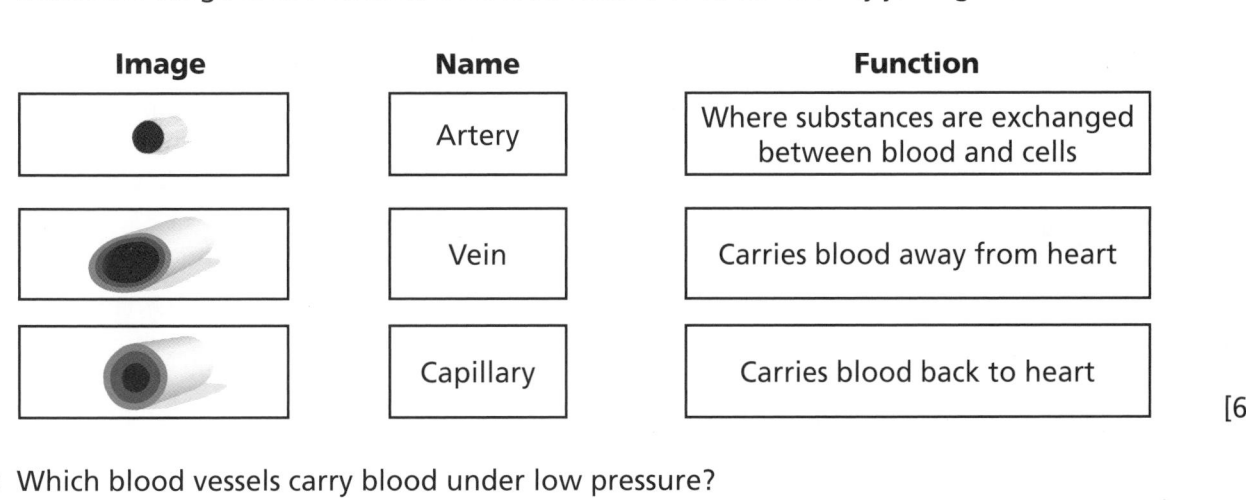

Image	Name	Function
	Artery	Where substances are exchanged between blood and cells
	Vein	Carries blood away from heart
	Capillary	Carries blood back to heart

[6]

b) Which blood vessels carry blood under low pressure?

_____ [1]

c) Which blood vessels have valves?

_____ [1]

d) The diagram shows a network of capillaries in a muscle.

Tick (✓) the boxes next to the two substances that are most likely to be found in the blood flowing through an artery?

Carbon dioxide	
Glucose	
Urea	
Starch	
Oxygen	

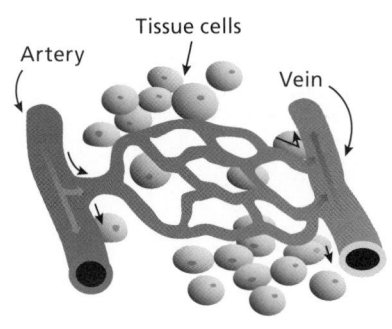

Tissue cells

Artery

Vein

[2]

> **Total Marks** _____ / 12

The Heart and Blood Cells

1 The diagram shows a human heart.

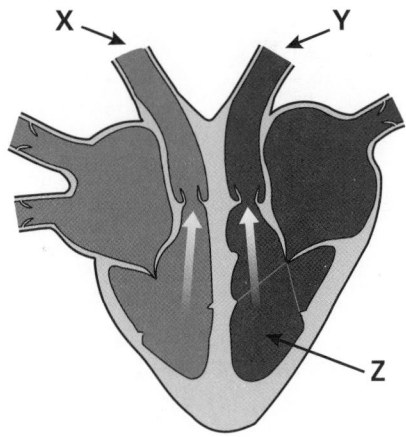

The bottom chambers are contracting, forcing blood through the blood vessels labelled **X** and **Y**.

a) What name is given to the bottom chambers of the heart

.... [1]

b) Are blood vessels **X** and **Y** arteries or veins?

Explain your answer.

....

.... [2]

c) Where is blood flowing to when it flows through blood vessel **X**?

.... [1]

d) How is the chamber labelled **Z** adapted to its function?

....

....

.... [3]

2 Name **three** substances carried by plasma.

.... [3]

Total Marks .... / 10

Plants, Water and Minerals

1 The diagram below shows two similar plants in different conditions.

Plant X

Plant cells short of water so the plant wilts

Not enough water in soil

Plant Y

H_2O H_2O
H_2O
H_2O
H_2O
H_2O

Plant cells full of water so the plant stays erect

Plenty of water in soil

Plants lose water through pores in the leaf called stomata.

a) In which plant will the stomata be closed?

_____ [1]

b) Explain why plant **X** will not be photosynthesising.

_____ [2]

c) Which terms describes the cells of plant **Y**?
   Tick (✓) the correct answer.

Turgid	
Flaccid	
Wilting	

[1]

d) Water moves from the roots to the leaves before being lost from the leaves.

   What is this process called?

_____ [1]

e) How do the following factors affect water loss from a plant's leaves?

   i) Wind speed _____ [1]

   ii) Temperature _____ [1]

f) The diagram shows a stoma.

   What is the role of the cell labelled **A**?

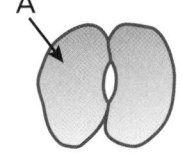

A

_____ [1]

g) Explain why it is usual to find more stomata on the lower surface of a leaf compared with the upper surface.

_____

_____ [2]

Total Marks _____ / 10

Coordination and Control

1 Match the part of the nervous system to its function by drawing a line between them.

Nervous System Part   **Function**

| Sensory neurone |

| Carries impulses from relay neurone to effector |

| Receptor |

| Carries impulses from receptor to relay neurone |

| Brain |

| Detects a stimulus |

| Motor neurone |

| Responsible for coordinating a response | [3]

2 The diagram below shows a neurone.

Impulse travels towards cell body and then away from cell body

What type of neurone is it?

_____   [1]

3 The diagram shows the junction between two nerve cells, **A** and **B**. The arrow shows the direction of the nerve impulse.

Complete the passage below about transmission of nerve impulses by filling in the gaps.

A receptor receives a _____ and generates an _____ impulse in

the _____ neurone. The impulse travels along the neurone until it reaches a

_____ . The sensory neurone releases a chemical called a _____ .

This crosses the gap and binds to _____ on the next neurone. This generates

another electrical impulse.   [6]

4 Which statement is true for a nervous response? Tick (✓) one box only.

A very quick response	
A generalised response	
Carried by chemical impulses	
Long-lasting effect	

[1]

Total Marks _____ / 11

The Eye and the Brain

1 **a)** Use the words below to label the diagram of the eye.

retina   lens   iris   optic nerve

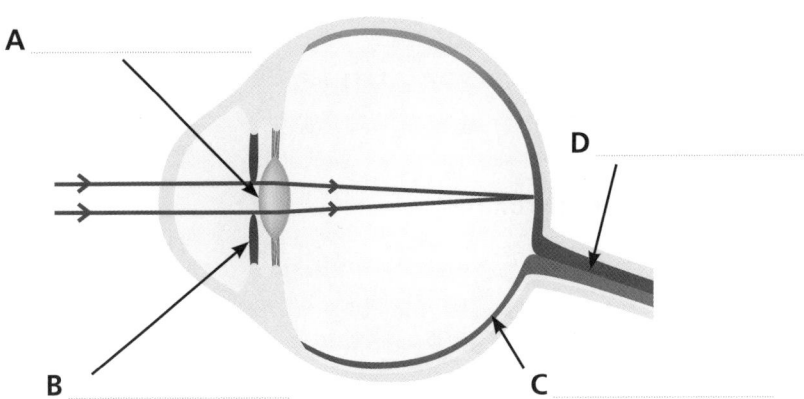

[4]

b) If a bright light is shone into the eye, the pupil becomes smaller.

What type of reaction is this?

.... [1]

2 **a)** Paul is red–green colour blind.

Underline the correct word(s) to complete the sentence below.

Colour blindness is **inherited** / **caused by a pathogen** / **a result of a vitamin deficiency**. [1]

b) Donna is short sighted. She visits the opticians for some new glasses.

What type of lenses will the optician use in her glasses?

.... [1]

Total Marks .... / 7

The Endocrine System

1 The diagram shows the major glands in the body that produce hormones.

a) What is the name of gland **C**?

_____ [1]

b) Name the **two** hormones produced by gland **A**.

_____ [2]

c) Which hormone causes gland **D** to produce thyroxine?

_____ [1]

d) The glands labelled **E** are found on top of which organs?

_____ [1]

e) The organs labelled **F** produce the male sex hormone.
What are the organs called?

_____ [1]

f) How do hormones travel to their site of action?

_____ [1]

2 Which of the following statements are true about hormones? Tick (✓) two boxes.

They are fast acting	
They are chemicals	
They are proteins	
Their response is long lasting	

[2]

3 The following flow diagram is about control of blood glucose levels.

a) Process **A** happens in which organ?

_____ [1]

b) Process **B** happens in which organ?

_____ [1]

Blood glucose levels rise
↓
A Insulin produced
↓
B Glucose converted to glycogen
↓
C Increased permeability of membrane to glucose

c) When blood glucose levels return to normal, insulin production stops.
What is this an example of?

_____ [2]

Total Marks _____ / 13

Hormones and Their Uses

1 A woman's fertility can be controlled by drugs made from female sex hormones.

a) What hormone can be combined with oestrogen in the female contraceptive pill?

[1]

b) What hormone stimulates the release of the egg?

[1]

2 Read the following passage about the use of hormones to control fertility.

> Hormones can be given to women to control their fertility. The contraceptive pill allows women to choose when to have children. They may wish to delay having children while developing a career or until they can afford to have children.
>
> Not everyone can take the pill. It can cause side effects in some people and there are some religions that feel it is wrong for humans to control their fertility.
>
> Hormones can also be used to help women who are struggling to conceive. They can be given to stimulate the release of eggs, which can be fertilised naturally or by in vitro fertilisation (IVF).
>
> IVF is expensive and has less than a 50% success rate but does allow infertile couples to have their own children rather than adopt. Sometimes two or more embryos are fertilised successfully, resulting in multiple births. Embryos produced by IVF can be screened for genetic diseases before being implanted in the womb. Embryos not implanted can be used for research or are destroyed.

a) Which **two** hormones might be used in fertility treatment?

[2]

b) Give **two** arguments against taking the contraceptive pill.

[2]

c) Discuss the advantages and disadvantages of IVF.

[6]

Total Marks _____ / 12

Plant Hormones

1 Complete the passage below about plant hormones by choosing the correct words below. You do **not** have to use all the words.

shoots   **light**   **growth**   **roots**   **temperature**   **germination**

Auxin is a plant hormone that controls plant _____. In _____, auxin

encourages cells to elongate. In _____, auxin inhibits growth of cells. Auxin is

responsible for a plant's response to _____.   [4]

2 A student germinated a bean seed.
Diagram **A** shows the bean after 7 days.
The student then turned the bean onto its side (diagram **B**).
Diagram **C** shows the bean a week later.

A   B   C

a) On diagram **A**, label the root and shoot.   [2]

b) Explain why the plant responded this way.

_____

_____

_____   [2]

3 Match the plant hormone to its use by drawing a line between them.

Hormone	Use
Gibberellin	Ripening fruits
Auxin	Ending seed dormancy
Ethene	Rooting powder

[2]

Total Marks _____ / 10

Maintaining Internal Environments

1 The internal temperature of the body needs to be kept constant.

a) What is the normal body temperature of humans?

_____ [1]

b) Enzymes have an optimum temperature at which they work.

Explain what happens to the enzymes if the temperature of the body:

i) increases _____ [1]

ii) decreases _____ [1]

c) Which part of the body monitors the temperature of the blood?

_____

d) The diagrams below show the response of blood vessels in the skin to hot or cold conditions.

Greater blood flow through superficial capillary

Shunt vessel constricted

A

Reduced blood flow through superficial capillary

Shunt vessel dilated

B

Which diagram shows the skin on a cold day? _____ [1]

e) Suggest **two** other ways the body responds to cold weather.

_____ [2]

2 Describe the similarities and differences between type 1 and 2 diabetes.

_____

_____

_____ [3]

<table>
<tr><td>Total Marks _____ / 9</td></tr>
</table>

Water and the Kidneys

1 Water intake and water loss by the body need to be balanced.

a) Name **two** ways that the body takes in water.

.... [2]

b) Name **two** ways water is lost from the body.

.... [2]

c) Which organ is responsible for monitoring the water content of the blood?

.... [1]

d) When the water content of the blood drops, the hormone ADH is produced.

What is the effect of ADH on the kidneys?

.... [1]

e) The diagram below shows the part of the kidney that filters the blood.

i) What is name of this part of the kidney?

.... [1]

ii) Which letter represents the glomerulus?

.... [1]

iii) What happens at point **B**?

.... [1]

f) Which of the following should not be present in urine?
Tick (✓) the correct box.

Water	
Ions	
Urea	
Glucose	

[1]

Total Marks .... / 10

Recycling

1 **a)** In the carbon cycle, carbon is returned to the atmosphere by the respiration of **three** groups of organisms.

What are the three groups?

_____

_____

_____ [3]

b) Which molecule do plants convert atmospheric carbon dioxide into during photosynthesis?

_____ [1]

2 **a)** Some plants have nitrogen fixing bacteria in their root nodules.
This bacteria can turn nitrogen into nitrates.

What natural process also fixes nitrogen?

_____ [1]

b) Plants need nitrogen to make certain kinds of molecules.

What are these molecules?

_____ [1]

> **Total Marks** _____ / 6

Decomposition and Interdependence

1 The diagram shows a farmland food web.

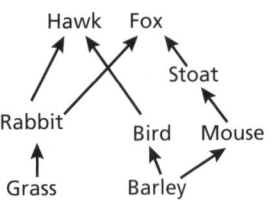

a) Name **two** animals that are in competition with each other for food.

_____ [1]

b) Name **one** primary consumer from the web.

_____ [1]

c) Name **one** producer from the web.

_____ [1]

2 The graph shows the population of foxes in a woodland over time.

a) Suggest **three** reasons for the decrease in fox numbers at point **A**.

_____

_____

_____

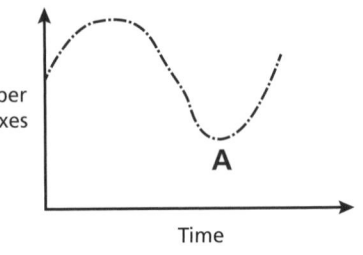

[3]

b) Give **three** resources for which foxes will compete.

_____ [3]

c) The trees in the woodland will also be in competition with each other. Give **three** resources for which trees will compete.

_____ [3]

3 The image shows a buffalo and some oxpecker birds. The birds feed on tiny parasites on the buffalo's skin.

a) What sort of relationship is this?

_____

_____ [1]

b) Marcus says that the oxpecker bird is a parasite.

Why is Marcus wrong?

_____

_____ [1]

Total Marks _____ / 14

Biomass and Energy Transfers

1 A free range hen is free to run around. The diagram shows the energy intake and expenditure for a free range hen.

a) **A** shows an energy loss of 60%.

Suggest how this energy is lost.

_____ [1]

b) What percentage of energy is available for growth and egg production?

_____ [1]

c) The hen consumes 20 000kJ of energy in a week.

Work out how much energy is available for growth and egg production.

_____ [2]

d) Some poultry farmers keep hens in heated barns.

Suggest why they heat the barns.

_____

_____ [2]

2 The following food chain is found in a greenhouse owned by Mr and Mrs Taylor.

tomato plants ⟶ aphids ⟶ ladybirds

a) Draw a pyramid of biomass for the food chain in the box to the right. [2]

b) Mr Taylor is worried about the aphids destroying the tomato plants so he buys some insecticide to spray on the plants. Mrs Taylor does not want to use insecticide.

Suggest a reason why Mrs Taylor might not want to use insecticide.

_____ [1]

Total Marks _____ / 9

Genes

1 Complete the following sentences by filling in the missing words.

An inherited characteristic is controlled by _____, which are found on structures

called chromosomes. Chromosomes are made of _____ which is coiled to form a

_____ _____. Body cells have pairs of chromosomes and are said to be

diploid, while gametes have single chromosomes and are said to be _____. **[4]**

2 The diagram shows one way that the strawberry plant can produce offspring.

Which statement is true? Tick (✓) the correct box.

The offspring is a clone of the parent	
The cells of the offspring will be haploid	
This is an example of sexual reproduction	

Runner

Offsping

[1]

3 Mendel was a scientist who carried out many investigations into breeding pea plants.

He concluded that the height of the pea plants was controlled by 'determiners' (which we
now know are genes) and that plants were always tall or short.

Mendel crossed two pure bred pea plants – one tall and one short and found that all the
offspring were tall.

a) Which is the dominant trait?

_____ **[1]**

b) Mendel then crossed two of the offspring and found that in the next generation the ratio
of tall to small plants was 3 : 1.

Draw a genetic cross to show why this happened. **[2]**

c) Mendel carried out more than 20 000 experiments on pea plants.

Why was it important he carried out so many experiments?

_____ **[1]**

Total Marks _____ / 9

Genetics and Reproduction

1 Chelsea is describing herself on a dating website.

I am 27 years old, 150cm tall and quite thin. I have blonde hair and blue eyes. I have my ears and eyebrows pierced. I work in a sports shop and am a very good swimmer.

a) Which **two** characteristics are inherited?

_____ [2]

b) Name **one** characteristic that is most likely due to a combination of inherited and environmental factors.

_____ [1]

2 Insulin is produced by special cells in the pancreas called beta cells.
The genes in the beta cells are the same as the genes in all body cells.

Explain why beta cells produce insulin but other body cells do not.

_____ [1]

3 Match the pairs of alleles to the correct description by drawing a line between them.

| tt | | Heterozygous |
| Tt | | Homozygous dominant |
| TT | | Homozygous recessive | [2]

4 A camel body cell has 70 chromosomes.

a) Following mitosis, how many chromosomes will each resulting cell have? _____ [1]

b) Following meiosis, how many chromosomes will each resulting cell have? _____ [1]

5 The 23rd pair of chromosomes in humans is responsible for determining sex.
Draw a genetic diagram to show how sex is determined. [3]

Total Marks _____ / 11

Natural Selection and Evolution

1 Darwin and Lamarck were both scientists with ideas about evolution.

Lamarck believed that animals changed during their lifetime to suit their conditions. He decided that the necks of giraffes grew longer during their lifetime because they kept stretching to reach leaves high in trees.

a) Explain why Lamarck's idea was wrong.

[2]

b) Although correct, why were Darwin's ideas about evolution not readily accepted?

[2]

2 The phylogenic tree shows the classification of some of the big cats together with their Latin names.

a) Jordan says the snow leopard will be more closely related to the clouded leopard than the tiger, because the tiger is not a leopard.

Explain why Jordan is **not** correct.

Lion
Panthera leo

Jaguar
Panthera onca

Leopard
Panthera pardus

Tiger
Panthera tigris

Snow leopard
Panthera uncia

[2]

Clouded leopard
Neofelis nebulosa

b) Scientists use fossil evidence to help classify organisms.

What other technique can they use that helps to show the evolutionary relationships between animals?

[1]

> **Total Marks** _____ / 7

Monitoring and Maintaining the Environment

1 Recent estimates suggest that if deforestation continues at its present rate, the world's rainforests will have vanished by the year 2150.

Explain why this is a problem.

[4]

2 **a)** A local conservation group claims that fertilisers from a nearby farm are responsible for the death of a large number of fish in a lake.

Suggest why they might think this.

[2]

b) Some students wanted to investigate the effect of different concentrations of fertiliser on the growth of broad bean plants.
They germinated 20 bean plants and selected five plants that had roots and shoots of the same length. They planted these in different pots and watered each pot weekly with a different concentration of fertiliser.
After 6 weeks, the students measured the height of the bean plants.
Their results are shown in the table below.

Concentration of Fertiliser %	0	2	4	6	8	10
Height of Bean Plant in cm	48	46	53	56	58	57

i) Give **two** variables that the students needed to control.

[2]

ii) In **one** sentence, write a conclusion for the students' results.

[2]

iii) Suggest how the students could improve the reliability of their results.

[2]

Investigations

1 A local wildlife group wanted to find out about the number of hedgehogs in an area.
They spent a night in the area and counted and marked each hedgehog they found.
A week later, they returned to the area and repeated the exercise. This time they
counted the hedgehogs and noted if they were marked or not.
On the first night 12 hedgehogs were counted and marked.
On the second night, 10 hedgehogs were counted, 6 of which were marked.

a) What is the name of the technique used by the wildlife group?

_____ [1]

b) Calculate the number of hedgehogs in the area.
Show your working.

_____

_____ [2]

c) Some members of the wildlife group were interested in butterflies.

What piece of equipment would be most suitable for sampling butterflies?

_____ [1]

2 Read the passage below about Kasanka in Zambia and answer the questions.

Thirty years ago, Kasanka was threatened by rampant poaching. There was no tourism,
little wildlife and little community development. A British expatriate, called David Lloyd,
visited the area and was so concerned that he applied for funding and permission to
develop the area. He built tourist camps, roads and bridges. He also set up Kasanka
National Park and Trust to raise funds for community-based projects and provide a safe
habitat for wildlife. Income from tourism goes towards park management and community
development. The community is involved in developing local schools, healthcare and
horticulture in the area. The local communities also sell local produce to tourists. The
trust promotes wildlife conservation, helps to enforce laws against poaching and helps to
maintain habitats. Today, wildlife and the local community are both flourishing.

a) Suggested **one** way that tourism has benefited the local community.

_____ [1]

b) How has the local environment and wildlife benefited from tourism?

_____

_____

_____ [2]

Total Marks _____ / 7

Feeding the Human Race

1 The world's population is increasing by around 90 million people each year.

Suggest **three** problems caused by increasing populations.

[3]

2 Genetic engineering involves modifying the genes of an animal or plant to introduce desirable characteristics. The diagram shows part of the process.

Section of donor DNA

Desired gene

A

Desired gene isolated

Desired gene inserted into target DNA

B

a) What type of enzyme is used at point **A**?

[1]

b) What type of enzyme is used at point **B**?

[1]

c) The desired gene is often inserted into bacterial hosts. Explain why bacteria are used.

[2]

d) Suggest why each of the following traits would be desirable

i) Maize that produces an insecticide in its leaves.

[1]

ii) Rice that contains high levels of vitamins.

[1]

Total Marks _____ / 9

Monitoring and Maintaining Health

1 Which of the following diseases are communicable diseases? Tick (✓) **three** correct boxes.

AIDS		Haemophilia	
Measles		Cholera	
Diabetes		Liver disease	
Cancer		Goitre	

[3]

2 Match each microorganism to its size and the disease that it causes by drawing lines between the boxes.

Type of Microorganism	Size	Disease
Virus	10μm	Thrush
Bacteria	1μm	Malaria
Protozoa	100μm	Tuberculosis
Yeast	0.1μm	Chickenpox

[4]

3 Plant pathogens usually enter plants through damaged tissues.

a) Give **two** causes of damage to plant tissue.

_____ [1]

b) Give **one** physical and **one** chemical defence mechanism in plants.

_____ [2]

4 A student needs to transfer some bacteria from the agar in a Petri dish to a glass slide so that she can observe the bacteria under the microscope.

Use the diagram to help explain how she will do this safely.

_____

_____

_____

_____

Bunsen burner

Petri dish

Agar

[4]

Total Marks _____ / 14

Prevention and Treatment of Disease

1 A tomato grower notices that some of his plants have yellowing leaves and are beginning to wilt.

These changes could be symptoms of either a bacterial or fungal infection.

a) State **two** ways in which the grower could find out what is causing the disease.

[2]

b) Suggest **two** steps the grower could take immediately to reduce the spread of the disease.

[2]

2 The human body has a number of mechanisms to prevent pathogens from entering.

a) Describe the role of platelets in defence to disease.

[2]

b) The respiratory system produces mucus.

What is the role of mucus in defence to disease?

[1]

3 **a)** Name **two** tests that may be carried out on new drugs before clinical trials.

[2]

b) In clinical trials, some patients are given the drug, and others are given a sugar pill that contains no drugs.

Explain why.

[2]

Total Marks .... / 11

Non-Communicable Diseases

1 By studying the human genome, scientists are able to predict the likelihood of an individual having a particular disease.

Potentially, this could be used to predict the chances of someone getting cancer.

Suggest **one** advantage and **one** disadvantage of being able to use the human genome in this way.

Advantage: ....

Disadvantage: .... [2]

2 Body mass index (BMI) is a simple measurement that is commonly used to classify a person as underweight, normal weight, overweight, or obese.

It is calculated using the following equation:

$$BMI = \frac{weight\,(kg)}{height^2\,(m)}$$

A BMI greater than or equal to 25 is overweight.
A BMI greater than or equal to 30 is obese.

Karanjit is 1.62 metres tall and weighs 74kg

a) Calculate Karanjit's BMI to one decimal place.

.... [2]

b) Name **two** health risks associated with obesity.

.... [2]

3 Some types of cancer can be treated by using monoclonal antibodies to deliver cancer drugs to the cancer cells.

What are the advantages of using monoclonal antibodies over conventional treatments such as radiotherapy therapy?

....

.... [2]

Total Marks .... / 8

Collins

GCSE (9–1)
Biology
Paper 1 (Higher Tier)

H

Time allowed: 1 hour 45 minutes

Instructions

- Use black ink. You may use a HB pencil for graphs and diagrams.
- Answer **all** the questions.
- Write your answer to each question in the space provided.
- Additional paper may be used if required.

Information

- There are **90** marks available on this paper.
- The marks for each question are shown in brackets [ ].
- Quality of extended response will be assessed in questions marked with an asterisk (*).

Practice Exam Paper 1

SECTION A

Answer **all** the questions.
You should spend a maximum of 30 minutes on this section.

1 The diagram shows a light microscope.

What is **X**?

A lens

B stage

C spine

D mirror   Your answer [ ] **[1]**

2 Which cell does not have a nucleus?

A red blood cell

B white blood cell

C neurone

D root hair cell   Your answer [ ] **[1]**

3 The statements below are about proteins.

Which statement is **not** true?

A Proteins are made from amino acids.

B Proteins are digested by amylase.

C Enzymes are proteins.

D Proteins are polymers. Your answer ☐ **[1]**

4 The following statements are about enzymes.

Which statement is **not** true?

A The optimum temperature for all enzymes is 37°C.

B All enzymes are biological catalysts.

C All enzymes have an active site.

D All enzymes are denatured by high temperatures. Your answer ☐ **[1]**

5 Villi are found in the small intestine.
They are important in the absorption of the products of digestion.

Which of the following statements is true about villi?

A Villi are destroyed by the nicotine in cigarette smoke.

B Villi have thick walls to aid absorption.

C Villi provide a large surface area for absorption of molecules.

D Villi absorb only glucose from the intestines. Your answer ☐ **[1]**

Turn over

6 The diagram shows a plant cell.

What is the name of this cell?

A root hair cell

B epithelial cell

C mesophyll cell

D palisade cell   Your answer [ ]   **[1]**

7 Where is meristematic tissue found?

A central nervous system

B peripheral nervous system

C bone marrow

D plant roots and shoot tips   Your answer [ ]   **[1]**

8 What form of RNA carries instructions from the nucleus to the ribosome?

A rRNA

B tRNA

C sRNA

D mRNA   Your answer [ ]   **[1]**

9   The diagram shows an egg cell.

An egg cell measures 80μm in diameter from point A to point B.

A student measured the diameter of the cell shown in the picture and found it was 32mm.

How many times larger is the diagram compared to a real cell?

A.　.B

A   4

B   40

C   400

D   4000   Your answer ☐ **[1]**

10   In protein synthesis, where does transcription happen?

A   nucleus

B   cytoplasm

C   mitochondria

D   cell membrane   Your answer ☐ **[1]**

11   The diagram shows a working muscle cell.

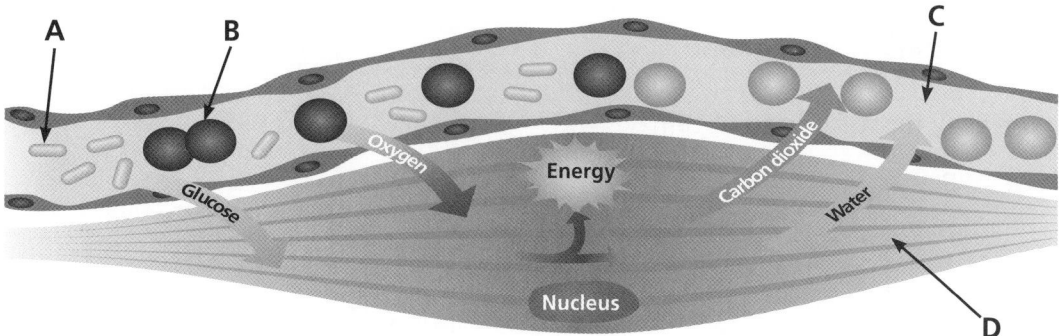

What letter is most likely to represent plasma?   Your answer ☐ **[1]**

Turn over

12 Terri looks at a piece of skin under a microscope using a high powered lens.
She can see cells, but is unable to see clearly the structures within the cells.

What is the most likely reason for this?

A The specimen is too thick.

B The resolution of the microscope is not high enough.

C The microscope is not focused correctly.

D There is insufficient light. Your answer [ ] **[1]**

13 DNA and RNA are involved in protein synthesis.
Protein synthesis involves transcription and translation.

Which row shows the molecules involved in each process?

	Transcription	Translation
A	mRNA and DNA	mRNA and tRNA
B	mRNA and DNA	tRNA and DNA
C	DNA	mRNA and tRNA
D	tRNA and DNA	mRNA and tRNA

Your answer [ ] **[1]**

14 Some students investigated the rate of reaction of amylase enzyme in turning starch into glucose.
They used temperatures between 0°C and 70°C.
They plotted their results as a line graph.

Which graph are they most likely to obtain?

   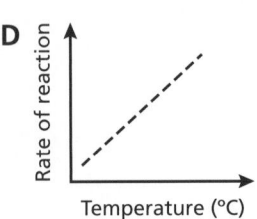

Your answer [ ] **[1]**

15 The diagram shows the position of nodes on a plant.
Plants can be treated with gibberellins to increase the distance
between each leaf node.

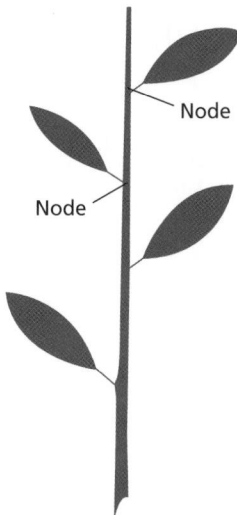

What is the purpose of doing this?

A To produce plants with bigger leaves.

B To produce dwarf plants.

C To strengthen the stem.

D To make dwarf plants grow into normal plants.

Your answer ☐ **[1]**

Turn over

SECTION B

Answer **all** the questions.

16 Some students were investigating the effect of light on the growth of a plant shoot.

They took four plants and placed them in different boxes as shown below.

Box lit from top

Box lit from top

Box lit from side

Box lit from side

A

B

C

D

Tip of shoot covered with black plastic

Tip of shoot covered with black plastic

After a week, Plant **C** was bending towards the light source.

The other three plants continued to grow upright.

(a) Explain why Plant **C** responded in this way but the other plants did not.

[3]

(b) Conor and Lewis wanted to find out how different concentrations of the plant hormone ethene affected tomatoes.

They treated batches of 20 tomatoes with the hormone and worked out the percentage that ripened within 24 hours.

They recorded their results in a table.

Concentration of ethylene used %	0	1	2	3	4	5
% of tomatoes that ripened	20	35	60	95		95

(i) When they used 4% ethene, Conor counted 18 tomatoes that had ripened.

Write this in the table as a percentage.   [1]

(ii) Lewis counted 17 ripe tomatoes using a concentration of 4% ethene.

Suggest why Conor and Lewis had different results.

....

.... **[1]**

(iii) Write a conclusion for the experiment.

....

....

....

.... **[2]**

(c) The plant hormone gibberellic acid can be used to overcome dormancy in seeds and buds.
In seeds, it stimulates the production of amylase enzyme.

Suggest how this helps to overcome dormancy.

....

....

....

.... **[3]**

Turn over

17 Catalase is an enzyme that breaks down hydrogen peroxide to release oxygen gas.

Catalase is present in liver.

Some students wanted to investigate the effect of pH on catalase activity.

They took five boiling tubes and placed a piece of liver in each.

They then added to each tube hydrogen peroxide that had been buffered to a different pH.

The students counted the number of bubbles produced in five minutes.

(a) Why is counting bubbles **not** an accurate way of measuring the amount of oxygen produced?

[2]

(b) Another group of students carried out the same experiment but decided to collect the oxygen using a gas syringe.

(i) Explain why this will give a more accurate measure.

[1]

(ii) Name **three** variables the students should control in the experiment.

_____

_____

_____ **[3]**

(iii) On the axis below, sketch the graph you would expect to get from the results.

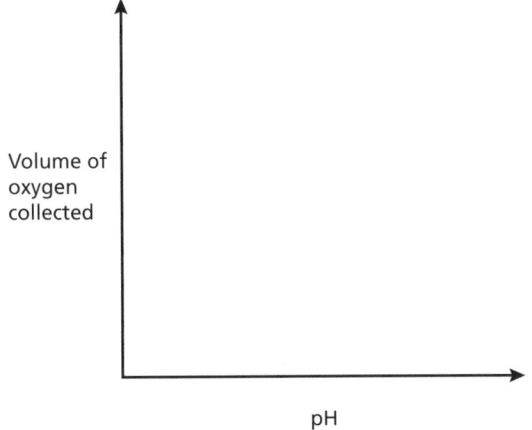

pH

[1]

18 Some students wanted to investigate the link between surface area to volume ratio (SA : V) and rate of diffusion.

They found the following information in a textbook.

Side length of cube	Surface area	Volume	SA : V ratio
2cm	2 × 2 × 6 = 24cm²	2 × 2 × 2 = 8cm³	24 to 8 = 3 : 1
4cm			
6cm	6 × 6 × 6 = 216cm²	6 × 6 × 6 = 216cm³	216 to 216 = 1 : 1
8cm	8 × 8 × 6 = 384cm²	8 × 8 × 8 = 512cm³	384 to 512 = 0.75 : 1

(a) Complete the table for the cube with a side length of 4cm. [3]

(b) In which cube will diffusion occur fastest?

Explain your answer.

[2]

(c) Explain why large multicellular organisms require specialised systems, such as the respiratory system, but unicellular organisms do not.

[2]

19 Adam, Ben and Tommy want to find out who has the quickest reactions.

They use a computer programme.

When they see the shape change from green to red, they have to press the mouse button as quickly as they can. The computer calculates their reaction times and puts them in a table.

User name	1st attempt	2nd attempt	3rd attempt	Mean average
Adam	0.52	0.49	0.46	0.49
Ben	0.66	0.62	0.61	
Tommy	0.45	0.42	0.42	0.43

(a) Calculate the mean for Ben's results.

....

.... [2]

(b) What is the relationship between reaction time and number of attempts? [1]

(c) In this experiment, the pupils are making a voluntary response.

Write down the stages of the pathway represented by **A**, **B** and **C**. [3]

receptor $\longrightarrow$ **A** $\longrightarrow$ relay neurone $\longrightarrow$ **B** $\longrightarrow$ **C** $\longrightarrow$ response

A ....

B ....

C ....

(d) Another group of students wanted to find out the effect of caffeine on reaction times.
They divided the class into five groups.
The first group drank 100cm³ of caffeine-free cola. The other four groups each drank different volumes of cola containing caffeine.
After 10 minutes, the students in each group tested their reaction times on the computer and found the average time.

The results are shown in the table.

Group	1	2	3	4	5
Amount of cola with caffeine (cm3)	0	100	150	200	250
Average reaction time (s)	0.52	0.48	0.47	0.40	0.37

Turn over

(i) Plot a line graph of the results. [3]

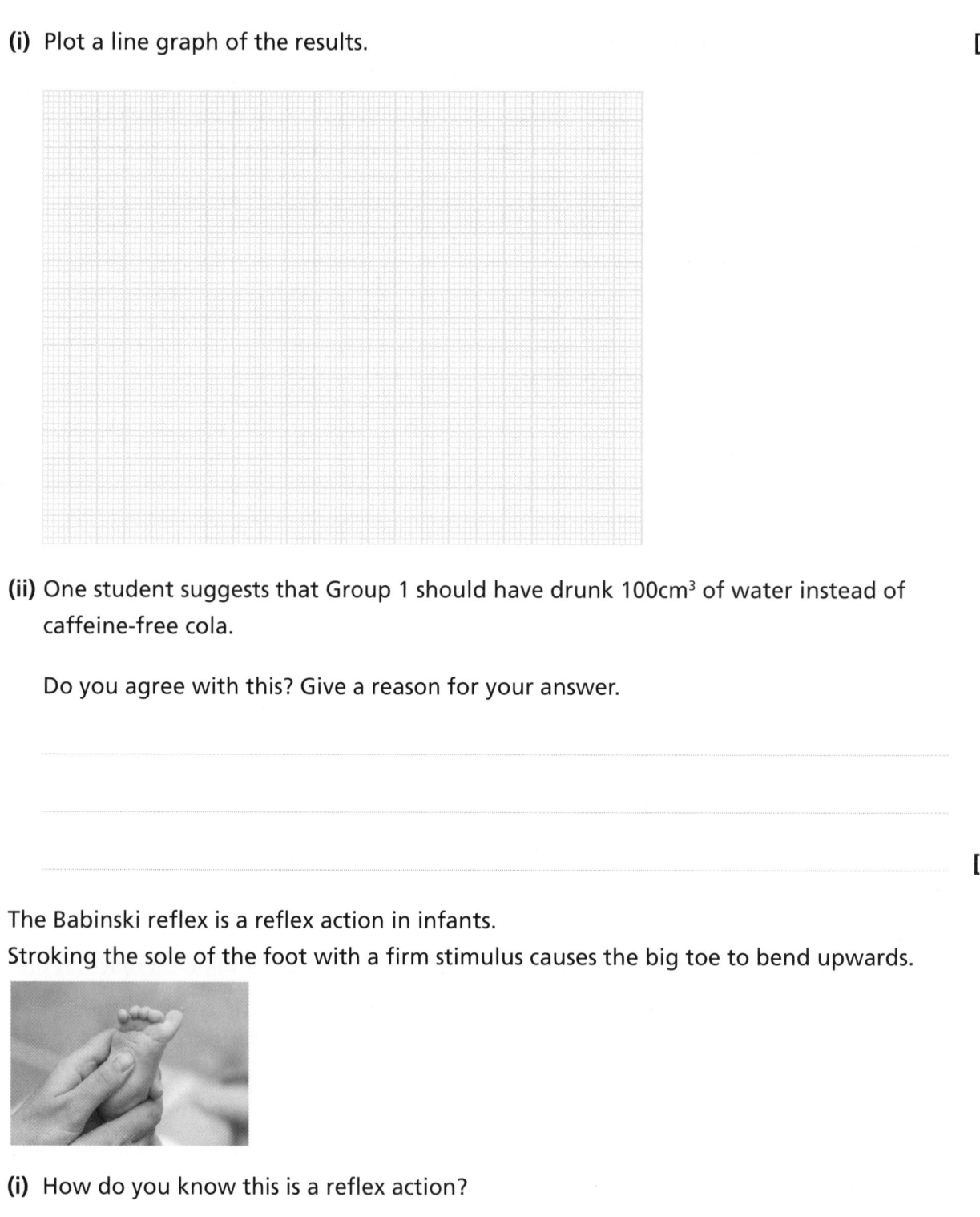

(ii) One student suggests that Group 1 should have drunk 100cm³ of water instead of caffeine-free cola.

Do you agree with this? Give a reason for your answer.

_____

_____

_____ [1]

(e) The Babinski reflex is a reflex action in infants.
Stroking the sole of the foot with a firm stimulus causes the big toe to bend upwards.

(i) How do you know this is a reflex action?

_____

_____ [1]

(ii) What is the function of the reflex action?

_____

_____ [1]

20 Some children are born with a hole in the heart.

When this happens, there is a hole at point **X** on the diagram, between the left and right side of the heart.

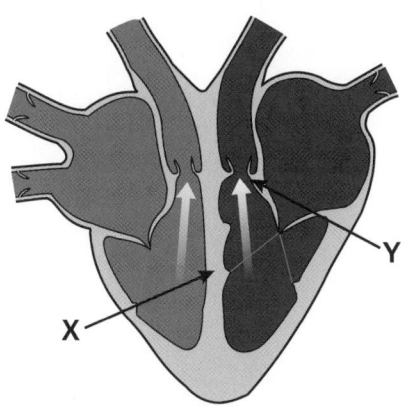

Dionne is 13 years old. She has had a hole in the heart since she was born.
She easily gets short of breath and finds physical exercise very tiring.

(a) Explain why she has these symptoms.

_____

_____

_____

_____

_____ **[2]**

(b) Aortic valve stenosis is when the valve labelled **Y** is too narrow.

What will be the likely effect of this condition on the heart?

_____

_____ **[1]**

Turn over

(c) When heart valves become damaged they may need to be replaced with either mechanical (artificial) valves or tissue (animal donor) valves.

There is a higher risk of blood clots when mechanical valves are used and patients will need to take blood thinning medication for the rest of their lives.

Valves from animal donors usually only last a maximum of 20 years.

Using stem cell technology, it is hoped that replacement heart valves could eventually be grown from a person's own cells.

(i) What is the function of heart valves?

[1]

(ii) Suggest **two** reasons why someone might be reluctant to have a heart valve from an animal donor.

[2]

(iii) What are the advantages of using stem cells to produce heart valves?

[2]

21 In 1921, two scientists called Banting and Best performed a number of experiments on dogs.
In their first experiment they removed the pancreas from a dog.
The dog's blood glucose levels rose and the dog developed diabetes.
In a second experiment, they removed a pancreas from a healthy dog, froze it, ground it and filtered it.
The filtrate they extracted was injected into the diabetic dog with high blood glucose levels.
The dog's blood glucose levels returned to normal and it became healthier.

(a) What substance had Banting and Best discovered.

_____ **[1]**

(b) Glucose is needed for respiration.

Complete the symbol equation below for aerobic respiration.

$C_6H_{12}O_6$ +   _____ $\rightarrow$ $6CO_2$ +   _____   **[2]**

(c) Yeast respires anaerobically to produce alcohol.
Colin wanted to make some homemade pear wine.
He mashed some pears, added water, yeast and sugar and left the mixture for a week.

   (i) Why did Colin add sugar?

_____

_____ **[1]**

   (ii) After a week, Colin noticed a lot of bubbles in the mixture.

Explain why there were bubbles.

_____

_____ **[1]**

(d) Describe the differences between aerobic and anaerobic respiration in humans.

_____

_____

_____

_____

_____ **[4]**

Turn over

(e) Why do muscle cells contain a high number of mitochondria?

....

....

....

....
 [2]

22 The photograph shows a water lettuce, which is a floating water plant.
It is not anchored to the ground, but has hair-like roots.

(a) Explain how water moves into the water lettuce.

[3]

(b) Water lettuce is a freshwater plant.

What would happen to the net movement of water if the water lettuce was placed in sea water?
Give a reason for your answer.

[2]

(c)* Explain how glucose and minerals are transported through a plant.

[6]

(d) In humans, blood is used to transport substances throughout the body.

Explain how oxygen is transported.

[2]

(e) Carbon dioxide is transported by blood plasma.

Name **three** other substances transported by plasma.

[3]

23 The table shows the composition of plasma and glomerular filtrate.

Substance	Concentration in plasma (arbitrary units)	Concentration in glomerular filtrate (arbitrary units)
Sodium	142	142
Urea	26	26
Proteins	4000	8
Glucose	100	100
Uric acid	3	3

(a) Why are so few proteins present in the glomerular filtrate compared with the plasma?

....

.... **[1]**

(b) Which of the substances in the table above will be present in urine in high concentrations?

....

.... **[1]**

(c) There are three forces that affect filtration at the glomerulus:

- Blood pressure in the capillaries forces fluid into Bowman's capsule.
  In a healthy individual this pressure averages 60mm of mercury.

- Fluid in the Bowman's capsule is pushed back into the capillaries with a pressure of 15mm mercury.

- The osmotic pressure of the blood draws fluid back into the blood at a pressure of 28mm of mercury.

Use the information above to calculate the net filtration pressure at the glomerulus.

Net pressure = ... **[2]**

END OF QUESTION PAPER

BLANK PAGE

Collins

GCSE (9–1)
Biology
Paper 2 (Higher Tier)

H

Time allowed: 1 hour 45 minutes

You may use:
- a ruler
- scientific calculator.

Instructions

- Use black ink. You may use a HB pencil for graphs and diagrams.
- Answer **all** the questions.
- Write your answer to each question in the space provided.
- Additional paper may be used if required.

Information

- There are **90** marks available on this paper.
- The marks for each question are shown in brackets [ ].
- Quality of extended response will be assessed in questions marked with an asterisk (*).

Practice Exam Paper 2

SECTION A

Answer **all** the questions.
You should spend a maximum of 30 minutes on this section.

1 Which of the following is an advantage of sexual reproduction?

A requires two parents

B provides genetic variation

C produces small numbers of offspring

D offspring may inherit diseases from parents   Your answer ☐ **[1]**

2 In a field there is a single oak tree.
Caterpillars eat the oak leaves.
The caterpillars are eaten by blackbirds.

Which diagram below shows the pyramid of biomass for this food chain?

A   B   C   D   Your answer ☐ **[1]**

3 An egg cell from a human female usually contains

A one X chromosome

B two X chromosomes

C one X and one Y chromosome

D one Y chromosome   Your answer ☐ **[1]**

4 Carla uses a quadrat to count the number of dandelion plants growing in different areas of a field.

Her results are shown below.

Quadrat number	Number of dandelions
1	7
2	9
3	8
4	8
5	6

Each quadrat measures one square metre.
The total area of the field is 60 square metres.

What is the estimated number of dandelions in the field?

A 98

B 228

C 380

D 456

Your answer ☐ [1]

5 Which of the following is an example of sustainable development?

A Introduction of fishing quotas that limit the amount of fish that can be caught.

B Clearing rainforests to grow food for the population.

C Imposing large taxes on fossil fuel use.

D Building museums to preserve the past.

Your answer ☐ [1]

Turn over

6 The diagram shows some stages in genetic engineering.

Part of a human DNA strand

Desired gene

Desired gene isolated

Desired gene inserted into target DNA

How is the desired gene inserted into the target DNA?

A using restriction enzymes

B using protease enzymes

C using ligase enzymes

D using lipase enzymes   Your answer ☐ **[1]**

7 Global sea levels have risen by about 17cm in the last century.

This is a result of

A volcanic activity

B global warming

C changes in rainfall patterns

D deforestation   Your answer ☐ **[1]**

8 Snails and slugs both feed on hosta plants.
Snails are eaten by the song thrush.

Which of the organisms below is a predator?

A snail

B slug

C hosta

D song thrush   Your answer ☐ **[1]**

9 An association between two individuals in which the association benefits both is called:

A mutualism

B competition

C commensalism

D parasitism

Your answer ☐ [1]

10 An example of a discontinuous variable is:

A height

B blood group

C weight

D width of hand span

Your answer ☐ [1]

11 The food web below is from a marine environment.

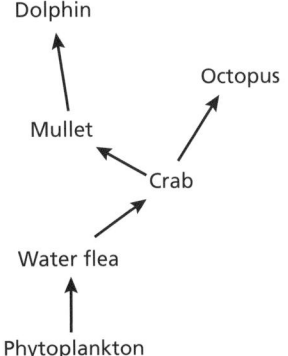

What is most likely to happen if there is overfishing of mullet?

A Dolphin numbers and crab numbers will decrease.

B Dolphin numbers will increase and crab numbers will decrease.

C Dolphin numbers decrease and crab numbers will increase.

D There will be no change in the numbers.

Your answer ☐ [1]

Turn over

12 Plants have physical defences to disease.

Which of these is an example of physical defence mechanisms in plants?

A production of toxins and antibacterial chemicals

B cells that produce lysozyme

C tough cell walls and waxy cuticles

D membranes that are selectively permeable   Your answer ☐ **[1]**

13 Monoclonal antibodies can be used to treat some types of cancer cells.
The diagram shows a cancer cell.

Which letter represents a monoclonal antibody?   Your answer ☐ **[1]**

14 What is non-coding DNA used for?

A switching genes on and off

B controlling dominant alleles

C controlling recessive alleles

D scientists have not discovered its function yet   Your answer ☐ **[1]**

15 A person who has been infected with human papilloma virus (HPV) has an increased risk of developing:

A tuberculosis

B influenza

C autism

D cervical cancer   Your answer ☐ **[1]**

SECTION B

Answer **all** the questions.

16 Look at the article from a nature magazine about ospreys.

> Although the osprey population has increased over recent years in the UK, they remain the fourth rarest bird of prey in the UK. They are at risk because they feed on fish and, therefore, depend on high water quality of rivers and lakes. Their eggs are often stolen by collectors and migrating ospreys are at risk from being shot by hunters.
>
>
>
> The Lake District Osprey Project has been running for several years to encourage these birds to breed in the UK. In 2001, a pair of ospreys nested beside Bassenthwaite Lake. They were the first wild osprey to breed in the Lake District for over 150 years. The Forestry Commission built a nest to encourage the birds to stay, which they did. Once the eggs were laid, wardens kept a round the clock watch to prevent disturbance and deter egg thieves. Bassenthwaite Lake is a National Nature Reserve and provides valuable habitats for a variety of wildlife.

(a) Ospreys were once endangered in the UK.

What does endangered mean?

_____

_____ [1]

(b) Give **one** way in which humans have caused the ospreys to become endangered.

_____

_____

_____ [1]

(c) How has the osprey been protected and encouraged to breed in the Lake District?

_____

_____

_____ [1]

Turn over

(d) Suggest a difficulty with running projects such as the one described.

_____

_____ **[1]**

(e) The fish that ospreys prey on feed mainly on microscopic plants called phytoplankton.

Draw a pyramid of biomass to show this food chain. **[2]**

17 The graph below shows the smoking habits and incidence of lung cancer for people living in a European country.

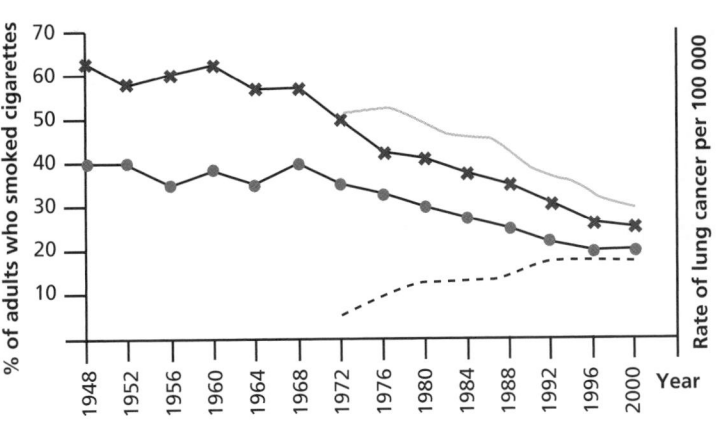

Smoking habits and lung cancer incidence in a European country

KEY

✖✖✖ Male smoking data

●●● Female smoking data

―――― Male incidence of lung cancer

- - - - Female incidence of lung cancer

(a) Describe the patterns in male and female smoking habits from 1948 to 2000.

....

.... **[2]**

(b) Calculate the percentage difference in female smokers between 1968 and 1988.

....

....

.... **[2]**

(c) Does the data support the hypothesis that smoking causes lung cancer? Give a reason for your answer.

....

....

.... **[2]**

Turn over

(d) A healthy heart is essential for good health.

How does each of the following affect the cardiovascular system?

(i) A diet high in fat

....

.... **[1]**

(ii) A diet high in salt

....

.... **[1]**

18 Below is one of the stages in the carbon cycle.

carbon in dead animals and plants ⟶ carbon dioxide in the atmosphere

(a) Explain the role of detritivores and decomposers in this stage.

....

....

.... [2]

(b) This process is likely to happen faster in a forest compared with a desert.

Explain why.

....

....

.... [2]

(c) Nitrogen is another element that is recycled.
Below is part of the nitrogen cycle.

nitrates in soil ⟶ nitrogen in the air

(i) Which type of bacteria is involved in this process?

....

.... [1]

(ii) Plants cannot use nitrogen gas.

What substance must nitrogen be converted into so that plants can
make use of it?

....

.... [1]

Turn over

19 The table contains information about three mammals.

Animal	Binomial name	Diet
Horse	*Equus ferus*	Eats grasses and plant materials. Has only one simple stomach.
Deer	*Dama dama*	Eats shoots, fresh grass, twigs, fruit. Has a complex stomach and can bring food back up into its mouth to chew again.
Zebra	*Equus zebra*	Eats mainly grasses. Has one simple stomach.

(a) Which two animals are most closely related?

Give **two** reasons for your answer.

....

....

....

[2]

(b) The table gives some information about donkeys and horses.

Donkeys	Horses
Stubborn but hard working	Hard workers
Sure footed	Delicate legs
Difficult to train	Easy to train
Slower runners	Fast runners
Average life span 30–50 years	Average life span 25–30 years
Ferments food in a hind gut so less prone to colic	Cannot vomit so prone to colic
Not very intelligent	Intelligent

A mule is a cross between a donkey and a horse.

Mules are often used to carry heavy loads on their backs in mountainous regions.

List the qualities required from the donkey and the horse to make the mule suitable for this work.

(i) Qualities from the donkey

....

....

....

[2]

(ii) Qualities from the horse

[2]

(c) A donkey has 62 chromosomes and a horse has 64 chromosomes.

(i) Explain why mules cannot breed.

[2]

(ii) It is wrong to call a mule a 'species'.

Explain why.

[1]

(d) Scientists believe the modern day horse evolved from a horse with four toes.
The four toes were useful for spreading the load on a soft forest floor.
As the ground hardened, a large central toe, similar to the hoof of today's horses,
was better for running over open country.

Using Darwin's theory of evolution, suggest how the modern day
horse with a hoof could have evolved.

[4]

Turn over

20 In aquatic environments, food chains start with microscopic green plants called phytoplankton. These are eaten by microscopic animals called zooplankton.

The pyramids of biomass show the mass of the organisms in summer and winter.

▬ Zooplankton
▢ Phytoplankton

Summer   Winter

(a) Explain why the biomass of phytoplankton changes between summer and winter.

[3]

(b) Small fish feed on zooplankton.
Gulls feed on small fish.
The diagram shows the amount of energy transferred at each trophic level.

2MJ   0.4MJ   44kJ

phytoplankton ⟶ zooplankton ⟶ small fish ⟶ gulls

(i) Calculate the energy efficiency of the transfer between small fish and gulls.

[2]

(ii) Sharks sometimes eat gulls.

Suggest how much energy might be transferred from the gull to the shark.
Give your answer in SI units.

[2]

(c)* Small fish are also eaten by tuna fish.

Tuna is one of the world's most widely eaten fish.

Large-scale fishing fleets use nets. Fishing fleets provide few opportunities for employment, profits are ploughed back into the company, there is always a bycatch (unwanted fish that are caught in the nets) and frequently tuna are overfished.

Many supermarkets now sell pole- and line-caught tuna.

This is one person with one pole or line catching one fish at a time.

Profits go back into the local community.

Describe a social, economic and environmental benefit of line and pole fishing compared to using commercial fleets.

[6]

21 The diagram shows sections of a pair of chromosomes from a cat, which contain genes for eye colour, ear shape and fur pattern.

Key
B Brown
b Blue
C Curled ears
c Straight ears
T Stripes
t tabby

(a) Describe the phenotype of the cat for these three characteristics.

....

....

.... **[3]**

(b) The cat above mates with a cat that is heterozygous for fur pattern.

(i) Complete the genetic cross diagram.

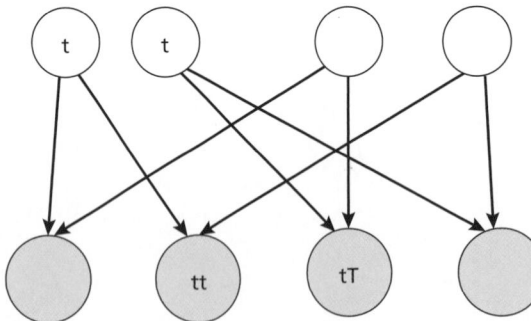

Parents tt Tt

Gametes t t

Offspring tt tT

[2]

(ii) What is the ratio of striped cats to tabby cats in the offspring?

....

.... **[1]**

(c) Polycystic kidney disease (PKD) is an inherited disease that affects cats.

Fluid-filled cysts are present in the kidneys from birth, but are so small initially that they go undetected.

As the cat gets older, the cysts become larger and eventually cause kidney failure.

In older cats, PKD can be detected by a scan of the kidneys.

PKD is controlled by a single pair of genes.

The allele for PKD is dominant.

A cat breeder is concerned that some of his kittens may have inherited PKD.

(i) How could he test to see if they had the condition?

_____

_____ [1]

(ii) Both parents of the kittens have developed PKU.

Draw a diagram to show the results of a cross if both parents are heterozygous for PKU. [3]

(iii) In a litter of eight kittens, how many kittens would you expect to have PKU if both parents were heterozygous for the condition?

_____

_____ [1]

Turn over

22 The diagram shows a bacterium called *P. aeruginosa*, which often causes infections of post-surgical wounds.

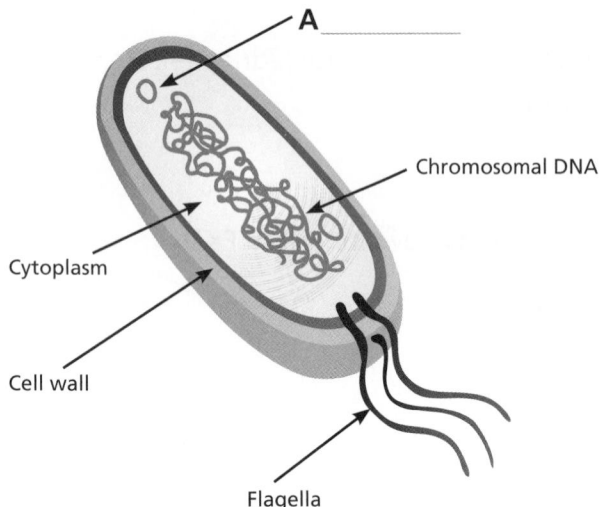

A

Chromosomal DNA

Cytoplasm

Cell wall

Flagella

(a) The structure labelled **A** is DNA that is separate from the chromosomal DNA.

On the diagram, write the name of structure **A**. [1]

(b) A patient has developed a post-surgical wound infection.
Some pus from the wound is examined and found to contain *P. aeruginosa*.
Doctors need to know which antibiotic will be best to treat the patient.
They spread the bacteria onto some agar in a Petri dish and add two filter paper discs that have been soaked in different antibiotics.
After incubation at 37°C they examine the Petri dish.
The diagram shows the actual size of the dish after incubation.

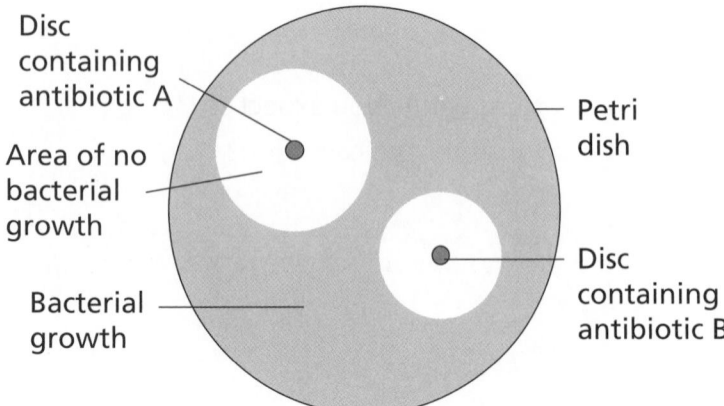

Disc containing antibiotic A

Area of no bacterial growth

Bacterial growth

Petri dish

Disc containing antibiotic B

If the area of no bacterial growth around the disc (including the disc) is greater than 200mm², the antibiotic can be used successfully to treat the infection.

(i) Work out if either or both of the antibiotics could be used to treat the infection. Use area of a circle = 3.14 × r².

[3]

(ii) In the school laboratory, bacteria should not be grown at 37°C.

Explain why.

[1]

(iii) Suggest **one** other factor that might determine which antibiotics should be used to treat an infection, other than whether the organism is sensitive or resistant to the antibiotic.

[1]

(c) Explain the action of phagocytic white blood cells when *P. aeruginosa* first enters a wound.

[3]

(d) *P. aeruginosa* can cause problems in hospitals because it easily develops resistance to a range of antibiotics.
Scientists would like to develop a vaccination that could be given to people at risk of post-surgical infections.

What would scientists use in the vaccination?

[1]

Turn over

23 The table shows the typical diets of people living in the developed countries of the Western world and people living in Eastern, developing countries.

Western diet	Eastern diet
Chicken, beef, lamb pork	Fish
Eggs, cheese, milk, cream	Milk
Processed cereals, cake, biscuits	Rice, corn, wheat, barley, noodles
Processed fish, convenience foods	Fruit

Over the past 10 years, many Eastern countries have begun to develop their economies and there has been a higher demand for a more Western diet, including more convenience foods.

(a) Describe the differences between a Western diet and a traditional Eastern diet.

[3]

(b) Why is the move towards a more Western diet likely to have a negative impact on local food supply?

[3]

(c) What are the implications of a more Western diet on health?
Give reasons for your answer.

[2]

END OF QUESTION PAPER

Answers

Workbook Answers

You are encouraged to show all your working out, as you may be awarded marks for method even if your final answer is wrong.

Page 148 – Cell Structure

1. a) Four correctly drawn lines [3] (2 marks for two correct lines; 1 mark for one)
   Nucleus – Contains genetic material
   Cell membrane – Contains receptor molecules
   Chloroplast – Contains chlorophyll
   Mitochondria – Contains enzymes for respiration
   b) Chloroplasts [1]
2. Higher resolution than light microscope [1]; Uses magnets to focus an electron beam [1]
3. a) Stain them [1]
   b) i) White blood cell / phagocyte [1]
      ii) Red blood cell [1]
   c) 4 × 100 = 400, ×400 magnification [1]

Page 149 – What Happens in Cells

1. DNA is made of two strands arranged as a double helix [1]; DNA is made of nucleotide [1]; Triplet codes in DNA code for amino acids [1]
2. a) Carbohydrates [1]
   b) fats / lipids [1]; fatty acids [1]; glycerol [1] (fatty acids and glycerol can be given in any order)
   c) A change in pH [1]
3. a) In this order: G, T, A, C, C [1]
   b) 3 / a triplet [1]
   c) Transcription [1]
   d) Nucleus [1]
4. Acid in stomach lowers the pH [1]; and denatures the enzyme [1]

Page 150 – Respiration

1. a) Bar chart drawn with each axis labelled [1]; appropriate scale [1]; two data sets clearly shown [1]; accurately drawn bars [1]

   b) Muscles will require more glucose and oxygen [1]; to release more energy during exercise [1]; these are delivered to cells by the blood [1]

   > Energy is **released**. Do not state that it is made or produced. This will lose you the mark.

2. a) Fungi [1]
   b) cell wall [1]; vacuole [1]
   c) glucose → ethanol + carbon dioxide [3] (1 mark for each correct chemical)
3. a) glucose + oxygen [1]; → carbon dioxide + water [1]
   b) In the blood [1]

   > When writing equations, make sure the reactants are to the left of the arrow and the products to the right.

Page 151 – Photosynthesis

1. a) Photosynthesis [1]
   b) Glucose [1]
   c) Respiration [1]; makes other molecules [1] (Accept named molecules, e.g. cellulose)
   d) At night, plants respire and produce carbon dioxide [1]; in the day, the plants respire but they will be also be photosynthesising, using up some carbon dioxide [1]

   > Remember, plants **respire** as well as **photosynthesise**.

2. a) water [1]; oxygen [1]
   b) $6H_2O$ [1]; $6O_2$ [1]
   c) Chloroplasts [1]
   d) Requires / takes in energy [1]
   e) Temperature [1]; concentration of carbon dioxide [1]

Page 152 – Supplying the Cell

1. a) B, E, A, C, D [1]
   b) Mitosis [1]
   c) Repair of tissues [1]
2. a) Diffusion: ← [1]
   b) Active transport: → [1]
   c) Osmosis: → [1]
3. a) bone marrow [1]; embryos [1]
   b) X = ciliated cell [1]; has cilia [1]; which move dirt and microorganisms up and out of respiratory system / move ova along the fallopian tubes [1]; Y = red blood cell [1]; concave shape increases the surface area [1]; for absorption of oxygen [1]; OR no nucleus [1]; so more room for carrying oxygen [1]

Page 153 – The Challenges of Size

1. a) Root hair cell [1]
   b) Leaf [1]
2. a) Six correctly drawn lines [6] (1 mark for each correct line)

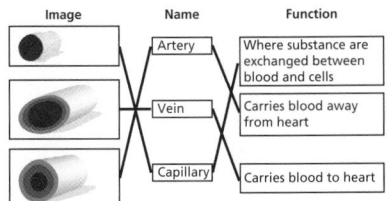

b) Veins [1]
c) Veins [1]
d) Glucose [1]; Oxygen [1]

> **Arteries** carry blood **away** from the heart. Remembering that both 'arteries' and 'away' start with the letter **A** should help you recall the right answer.

Page 154 – The Heart and Blood Cells

1. a) Ventricles [1]
   b) Arteries [1]; carry blood away from heart [1] OR X = pulmonary artery [1]; and Y = aorta [1]
   c) Lungs [1]
   d) Thick muscular walls [1]; for strong contractions [1]; to send blood under high pressure to body [1]
2. **Any three from:** carbon dioxide [1]; urea [1]; amino acids [1]; glucose [1]; antibodies [1]; hormones [1]

Page 155 – Plants, Water and Minerals

1. a) Plant X [1]
   b) Plants take in carbon dioxide for photosynthesis through stomata [1]; but stomata are closed to prevent water loss [1]
   c) Turgid [1]
   d) Transpiration [1]
   e) i) Increased wind speed increases water loss [1]
      ii) Increased temperature increases water loss [1]
   f) Guard cells open and close stomata [1]
   g) Underneath of leaf shaded / not in direct sunlight [1]; therefore less water will be lost through evaporation [1]

Page 156 – Coordination and Control

1. Four correctly drawn lines [3] (2 marks for two correct lines; 1 mark for one)
   Sensory neurone – carries impulses from receptor to relay neurone
   Receptor – Detects a stimulus
   Brain – Responsible for coordinating response
   Motor neurone – carries impulse from relay neurone to effector
2. Relay [1]

3. Stimulus [1]; electrical [1]; sensory [1]; synapse [1]; neurotransmitter [1]; receptors [1]
4. A very quick response [1]

Page 157 – The Eye and the Brain

1. a) A = lens [1]; B = iris [1]; C = retina [1]; D = optic nerve [1]
   b) Reflex [1]
2. a) inherited [1]
   b) Concave [1]

Page 158 – The Endocrine System

1. a) Pituitary [1]
   b) Insulin [1]; glucagon [1]
   c) Thyroid-stimulating hormone [1]
   d) Kidneys [1]
   e) Testes [1]
   f) In the blood [1]
2. They are chemicals [1]; Their response is long lasting [1]
3. a) Pancreas [1]
   b) Liver [1]
   c) Negative feedback [1]

Page 159 – Hormones and Their Uses

1. a) Progesterone [1]
   b) Oestrogen OR FSH [1]
2. a) Follicle-stimulating hormone (FSH) [1]; luteinising hormone (LH) [1]
   b) **Any two from:** Against some religious views [1]; can have side effects [1]; doesn't protect against STDs [1]
   c) **Any six from: Advantages:** allows infertile couples to have own children [1]; can screen embryos for genetic diseases [1]; embryos not used can be used in research [1] **Disadvantages:** expensive [1]; less than 50% success rate [1]; can result in multiple births [1]; ethical issues with what to do with unwanted embryos [1]

Page 160 – Plant Hormones

1. growth [1]; shoots [1]; roots [1]; light [1]
2. a) Correctly labelled root [1]; and shoot [1]

shoot

root

   b) Shoots are negatively geotropic / grow against gravity [1]; roots are positively geotropic / grow in the direction of gravity [1]
3. Three correctly drawn lines [2] (1 mark for one correct)

   Gibberellin – Ending seed dormancy
   Auxin – Rooting powder
   Ethene – Ripening fruits

Page 161 – Maintaining Internal Environments

1. a) 37°C [1]
   b) i) Denatured / destroyed [1]
      ii) Rate of reaction decreases / stops [1]
   c) Hypothalamus [1]
   d) B [1]
   e) Shivers [1]; hairs stand up [1]
2. **Any one from:** type 1 has an earlier onset, whereas type 2 tends to develop later in life [1]; in type 1 the pancreas does not produce insulin, whereas in type 2 the insulin is produced but not effective [1]; type 1 requires insulin injections, whereas type 2 can usually be controlled by diet [1] (Accept any other sensible comparisons)

Page 162 – Water and the Kidneys

1. a) Eating [1]; drinking [1]
   b) **Any two from:** sweating [1]; urinating [1]; breathing out [1]
   c) Brain [1]
   d) Causes the tubules to absorb more water [1]
   e) i) Nephron [1]
      ii) A [1]
      iii) Selective reabsorption [1]
   f) Glucose [1]

Page 163 – Recycling

1. a) animals [1]; plants [1]; microorganisms / decomposers [1]
   b) Glucose [1]
2. a) Lightning [1]
   b) Proteins [1]

Page 164 – Decomposition and Interdependence

1. a) Bird and mouse / hawk and fox [1]
   b) **Any one from:** rabbit [1]; bird [1]; mouse [1]
   c) Grass / barley [1]
2. a) Disease [1]; lack of food / prey [1]; introduction of new predator / hunted [1]
   b) **Any three from:** mates [1]; space / territory [1]; food [1]; water [1]
   c) **Any three from:** light [1]; water [1]; space [1]; nutrients [1]
3. a) Mutualism [1]
   b) The oxpecker bird is not harming the buffalo [1]

Page 165 – Biomass and Energy Transfers

1. a) As heat [1]
   b) $100 - 20 - 60 - 10 = 10\%$ [1]
   c) $\frac{20\,000}{100} \times 10$ [1] = 2000kJ [1]
   d) Hens will waste less energy keeping warm [1]; which means more energy for growth / egg production [1]

2. a) Correctly drawn pyramid [1]; labelled [1]

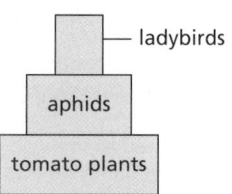

ladybirds

aphids

tomato plants

   b) Tomatoes may not be safe to eat / harmful to wildlife [1]

> Stating that food is not safe may not get you a mark. You need to be more specific and state it is not safe to **eat / consume.**

Page 166 – Genes

1. genes [1]; DNA [1]; double helix [1]; haploid [1]
2. The offspring is a clone of the parent [1]
3. a) Tall [1]
   b) Correct genotypes for both parents [1]; correct outcomes of cross [1] (Accept either a Punnett square or cross diagram)

Parent 1

		T	t
Parent 2	T	T T	T t
	t	T t	t t

   c) So he had sufficient evidence / to check repeatability of results [1]

Page 167 – Genetics and Reproduction

1. a) Blonde hair [1]; blue eyes [1]
   b) A good swimmer / thin / height [1]
2. In other body cells, the gene for insulin production is switched off [1]
3. Three correctly drawn lines [2] (1 mark for one correct line)
   tt – Homozygous recessive
   Tt – Heterozygous
   TT – Homozygous dominant
4. a) 70 [1]
   b) 35 [1]
5. Correct genotypes for both parents [1]; correct outcomes of cross [1]; identifying XX as female and XY as male offspring [1] (Accept a Punnett square or a cross diagram)

Mother

		X	X
Father	X	X X FEMALE	X X FEMALE
	Y	X Y MALE	X Y MALE

Page 168 – Natural Selection and Evolution

1. a) Characteristics are determined by genes [1]; which are inherited and present at birth [1]

b) Not enough evidence / genes had not been discovered [1]; his theory contradicted religious beliefs [1]
2. a) The snow leopard and tiger have evolved from a common ancestor [1]; who lived less time ago compared with the common ancestor of snow leopard and clouded leopard [1]
   b) DNA analysis [1]

Page 169 – Monitoring and Maintaining the Environment

1. Loss of habitat [1]; loss of biodiversity [1]; loss of potential medicines and drugs [1]; rainforests important in cycling carbon / removing excess carbon dioxide from the atmosphere through photosynthesis [1]
2. a) Fertilisers washed into lake [1]; leads to eutrophication (Accept description of eutrophication) [1]
   b) i) **Any two from:** size of pot [1]; amount / mass / type of compost [1]; size of beans [1]; light [1]; temperature [1]; length of roots and shoots [1]

   > Remember, giving an answer of compost is not sufficient to gain a mark. You need to be more specific, e.g. **mass** of compost or **type** of compost.

   ii) As the concentration of fertiliser increases, so does the height of the plants [1]; up to 8% [1]
   iii) Plant more beans at each concentration of fertiliser [1]; and calculate mean result [1]

Page 170 – Investigations

1. a) Capture–mark–recapture method [1]
   b) $\frac{12 \times 10}{6}$ [1]; $= \frac{120}{6} = 20$ [1]
   c) Sweep net [1]
2. a) Provides money for developing schools / health services [1]
   b) Income from tourism goes towards park / trust [1]; and is used to manage park / maintain habitats / enforce poaching laws [1]

Page 171 – Feeding the Human Race

1. **Any three from:** not enough food for everyone [1]; habitats lost to provide areas for people to live [1]; leading to reduced biodiversity [1]; increase in pollution (accept named pollutants) [1]
2. a) Restriction [1]
   b) Ligase [1]
   c) Plasmids easily inserted into bacteria [1]; bacteria multiply rapidly [1]
   d) i) Any insects trying to eat leaves will be killed so the crop isn't damaged [1]

ii) Could be used in developing countries where people are malnourished [1]

Page 172 – Monitoring and Maintaining Health

1. AIDS [1]; Measles [1]; Cholera [1]
2. All microorganisms correctly matched [1]; (2 marks if two are correctly matched; 1 mark if one is correctly matched)

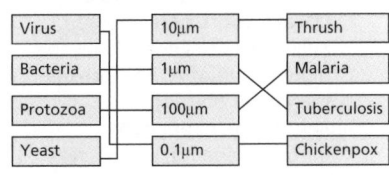

3. a) Animals trying to eat them / damage when being handled [1]
   b) Physical: tough cell wall / waxy cuticles [1]; Chemical: toxic chemicals / enzymes which kill / destroy pathogens [1]
4. Hold the loop in the flame to kill any bacteria [1]; allow loop to cool [1]; open Petri dish briefly and transfer bacteria from agar to slide with loop [1]; flame the loop [1]

Page 173 – Prevention and Treatment of Disease

1. a) Look at leaves under a microscope [1]; DNA analysis [1]
   b) Remove infected plants and ones nearby [1]; spray all plants with bactericide and fungicide [1]
2. a) Help blood to clot [1]; forms a scab, which prevents entry of microorganisms [1]
   b) Microorganisms and small particles of dirt are trapped by mucus [1]
3. a) **Any two from:** computer simulations [1]; tests on cells grown in laboratory [1]; tests on animals [1]; tests on healthy people [1]
   b) The sugar pill (placebo) is a control [1]; to compare the effect of using the drug and using no drug (with no psychological influences) [1]

Page 174 – Non-Communicable Diseases

1. Advantage: potential for people to change lifestyle / get early treatment / regular screening [1]
   Disadvantage: could lead to depression / people unable to get jobs / insurance (accept any other sensible answer) [1]
2. a) BMI = $\frac{-74}{1.62 \times 1.62}$ [1] = 28.2 [1]
   b) **Any two from:** heart disease [1]; stroke [1]; diabetes [1]; cancer [1]; joint / muscular problems / arthritis [1]
3. The drug can be delivered to cancer cells only [1]; no damage to healthy surrounding cells [1]

Page 175–196 – Practice Exam Paper 1

Section A
1. B [1]
2. A [1]
3. B [1]
4. A [1]

> The optimum temperature for enzymes in the human body is 37°C, but not for **all** enzymes.

5. C [1]
6. D [1]
7. D [1]
8. D [1]
9. C [1]
10. A [1]
11. C [1]
12. B [1]
13. A [1]
14. C [1]
15. D [1]

Section B
16. a) Auxin is produced in the tips of shoots and causes shoots to bend towards light [1]; B and D have tips covered so do not bend / no auxin is produced [1]; light source from A is from the top so no bending / tip grows upwards [1]

> When talking about auxin production, make sure you mention it is produced in the root / shoot **tip**. Tip is an important word - forget to use it and you may lose the mark.

   b) i) $\frac{18}{20} \times 100 = 90\%$ [1]
      ii) Idea that ripeness is difficult to measure, e.g. what colour is ripe, how much of the tomato needs to be ripe [1]
      iii) As the concentration of *ethylene*, increases [1]; a higher percentage of tomatoes ripen up to 3% [1]
   c) Amylase converts starch in seed to glucose [1]; since glucose is available, the seed can begin to respire and release energy [1]; for growth [1]
17. a) Bubbles could be different sizes [1]; individual bubbles difficult to count if produced quickly [1]
   b) i) Can measure volume of gas produced [1]
      ii) **Any three from:** amount / mass liver [1]; volume of hydrogen peroxide [1]; strength of hydrogen peroxide; time [1]; temperature [1]
      iii) A correct curve drawn [1]

18. a) Surface area = $4 \times 4 \times 6 = 96cm^2$ **[1]**; Volume = $4 \times 4 \times 4 = 64cm^3$ **[1]**; SA : V ratio = $\frac{96}{64}$ = 1.5 : 1 **[1]**

b) The 2cm / smallest cube **[1]**; because it has the largest surface area to volume ratio **[1]**

c) Large multicellular animals have a small surface area to volume ratio which decreases the rate of diffusion **[1]**; so they need specialised systems which take substances nearer to where they are needed, reducing the diffusion distance **[1]**

19. a) 0.66 + 0.62 + 0.61 = 1.89 **[1]**; $\frac{1.89}{3}$ = 0.63 **[1]**

b) The more attempts, the faster the reaction appears to be **[1]**

c) sensory neurone **[1]**; motor neurone **[1]**; effector **[1]**

d) i) Axes labelled and correct **[1]**; all points plotted correctly **[1]**; line of best fit (not a straight line from one point to next) **[1]**

Average reaction time (s) vs Amount of cola with caffeine (cm^3)

ii) No, there could be something in the cola other than caffeine that affected reaction times, therefore, control needs to be cola not water **[1]**

e) i) Happens automatically / no conscious decision made **[1]**

ii) To protect the body from pain / harm **[1]**

20. a) Some deoxygenated blood will pass through hole from right side to left side **[1]**; and be sent round body without going to the lungs **[1]** OR some oxygenated blood will pass from left side to right side **[1]**; so less oxygenated blood goes to the body **[1]**

b) The heart will have to work harder to force blood out, causing chest pain / feeling weak or dizzy when exercising **[1]**

c) i) To stop blood flowing backwards **[1]**

ii) Any two from: only last 20 years **[1]**; dislike idea of using non-human tissue **[1]**; chance of being infected with animal viruses **[1]**

iii) Should last longer **[1]**; no need to take antirejection medication **[1]**

21. a) Insulin **[1]**

b) $6O_2$ **[1]**; $6H_2O$ **[1]**

c) i) Carbon dioxide gas was produced **[1]**

ii) Sugar / glucose is a substrate for respiration **[1]**

d) Aerobic respiration happens in the mitochondria but anaerobic respiration happens in the cytoplasm **[1]**; aerobic is the complete breakdown of glucose but anaerobic is incomplete **[1]**; aerobic requires oxygen, anaerobic does not **[1]**; aerobic higher yield of ATP / more energy than anaerobic **[1]**

e) Respiration happens in mitochondria **[1]**; muscle cells need to release high amounts of energy for movement through respiration **[1]**

22. a) Water moves into root hair cells **[1]**; moving from area of high water concentration to area of low concentration **[1]**; by osmosis **[1]**

b) Net water movement would be out of plant **[1]**; because concentration of water would be higher in plant cells than outside **[1]**

c) Glucose moves by diffusion **[1]**; from areas of high concentration to areas of low concentration **[1]**; via the phloem tissue **[1]**; minerals enter plant by active transport **[1]** and move through plant due to the transpiration stream **[1]**; from roots to leaves through the xylem tissue **[1]**

> In the exam, if you see an asterisk (*) next to a question, it means that the quality of your response will be assessed. This means you must give all your ideas in a clear and logical way to avoid losing marks.

d) Inside red blood cells **[1]**; joined to haemoglobin / as oxyhaemoglobin **[1]**

e) Any three from: hormones **[1]**; antibodies; glucose **[1]**; amino acids **[1]**; minerals **[1]**; ions **[1]**; urea **[1]**

23. a) Too large to pass through walls of capillaries in glomerulus **[1]**

b) Urea / uric acid **[1]**

c) 60 – (28 + 15) **[1]**; = 17mm of mercury **[1]**

Page 197–216 – Practice Exam Paper 2

Section A

1. B **[1]**
2. D **[1]**
3. A **[1]**
4. D **[1]**

> $\dfrac{(7 + 9 + 8 + 8 + 6)}{5} = 7.6$
> $7.6 \times 60 = 456$

5. A **[1]**
6. C **[1]**
7. B **[1]**
8. D **[1]**
9. A **[1]**
10. B **[1]**
11. C **[1]**
12. C **[1]**
13. A **[1]**
14. A **[1]**
15. D **[1]**

Section B

16. a) At risk of extinction **[1]**

b) Any one from: hunting / taking eggs **[1]**; polluting lakes / rivers (which reduced food source) **[1]**

c) Any one from: nest built for breeding pairs **[1]**; wardens protect nests from disturbance / egg thieves **[1]**

d) Any one from: intense on labour **[1]**; high labour costs **[1]**; difficult to 'police' area **[1]**; has to be long-term project **[1]**

e) Correct shape of pyramid **[1]**; correctly labelled **[1]**

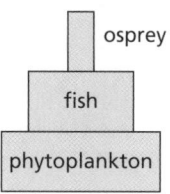

osprey / fish / phytoplankton

17. a) The number of male and female smokers has decreased steadily **[1]**; since 1968 **[1]**

b) 40 – 25 = 15 **[1]**; $\frac{5}{40} \times 100 = 37.5\%$ **[1]**

c) Yes – because as % of males who smoked decreased **[1]**; so did incidence of cancer in males **[1]** OR No – because as % females who smoked decreased **[1]**; the incidence of cancer increased **[1]**

d) i) Fat deposits build up and blocks arteries / increases risk of heart attack and strokes **[1]**

ii) Increases blood pressure **[1]**

18. a) Detrivores break matter into smaller pieces to increase surface area **[1]**; decomposers feed on dead matter and respire, releasing carbon dioxide **[1]**

b) In deserts there is less variety / fewer numbers of detritivores / fewer decomposers **[1]**; conditions very dry / less moisture **[1]**

c) i) Denitrifying **[1]**

ii) Nitrates **[1]**

> Sometimes students get confused and think that the decaying matter gives off carbon dioxide. It doesn't. **Respiration** of the **microorganisms / decomposers** which feed on the decaying matter is where the carbon dioxide comes from.

19. **a)** Horse and zebra: share same genus / both *Equus* [1]; both have simple stomach, whereas deer has complex stomach [1]

   b) **i)** Donkey: sure footed, less prone to colic, long life span, hardworking [2] (1 mark for more than two qualities; 2 marks for all qualities)

   ii) Horse: intelligent [1]; easy to train [1]

   c) **i)** Donkey gametes will have 31 chromosomes and horse gametes 32, which means mule cells will have 63 chromosomes [1]; 63 chromosomes cannot be halved in meiosis to produce gametes so mules are sterile [1]

   ii) Because species can breed with each other to produce fertile offspring [1]

   d) A mutation produced a horse with a larger central toe [1]; this horse was better at running so more likely to survive [1]; and breed [1]; and pass on genes to offspring [1]

20. **a)** In summer, phytoplankton reproduce rapidly due to warmth and light [1]; in winter, phytoplankton growth slows [1]; phytoplankton eaten by large numbers of zooplankton [1]

   b) **i)** $\frac{44}{400} \times 100$ [1]; = 11% [1]

   ii) 4400 [1]; joules [1]

   c) Social: creates more jobs [1]; which creates better standard of living [1]; Environmental: no overfishing [1]; so tuna populations maintained /

not endangered [1] OR Environmental: no bycatch [1]; other species not harmed / killed / maintains biodiversity [1]; Economic: more jobs [1]; brings money into the local community [1]

21. **a)** A tabby pattern [1]; with brown eyes [1]; and curled ears [1]

   b) **i)** Gametes: T and t [1]; offspring (in order): Tt and tt [1]

   ii) 1 : 1 [1]

   c) **i)** Genetic screening [1]

   ii) Correct genotypes of parents [1]; correct genotypes of offspring [1]; correct phenotypes of offspring [1] (Accept any correct genetic diagram)

Parent 1

		P	p
Parent 2	P	P P PKU	P p PKU
	p	P p PKU	p p no PKU

   iii) 6 [1]

> ¾ have PKU, so in a litter of 8 that would be 6 kittens with PKU.

22. **a)** Plasmid [1]

   b) **i)** Human pathogens / harmful bacteria could grow at this temperature [1]

   ii) Antibiotic A can be used, B cannot [1]

Disc A: radius in range of 8.5–9.5mm, so $8.5 \times 8.5 = 72.25 \times 3.14 = 226.9mm^2$ [1]; Disc B: radius in range 6.5–7.5mm, so $6.5 \times 6.5 = 42.25 \times 3.14 = 132.7mm^2$ [1]

   iii) Cost / if patient allergic to antibiotic [1]

   c) White blood cell engulfs the bacterium [1]; destroyed within white blood cell [1]; mention of phagocytosis or lysozyme or egestion of debris [1]

   d) Dead / weakened form of bacterium [1]

23. **a)** **Any three of following (answers must be comparative):** Western diet higher in fat [1]; Western diet more meat [1]; Eastern diet more fresh fish [1]; Western diet more processed foods [1]; Eastern more cereals [1]; Western diet higher in dairy / Eastern diet less dairy [1]

   b) Meat production is less energy efficient than eating plants [1]; more space needed to produce same yield of energy when farming animals compared to plants [1]; wastage when processing food [1]

   c) **Any two of following (but must have implication and reason for mark):** more heart disease because more fat in diet [1]; more high blood pressure / heart disease because salt added to processed foods [1]; increase in some cancers because of higher (red) meat content of diet [1]; increase obesity because high carbohydrate / fat diet [1]

Notes